941.31 Dou
410

CROSSING THE FORTH

By the same author

THE UNDERGROUND STORY

Crossing the Forth

by

HUGH DOUGLAS

*Illustrated
and with Maps*

ROBERT HALE LTD : LONDON

PRINTED IN GREAT BRITAIN BY
CLARKE, DOBLE AND BRENDON LTD.
CATTEDOWN, PLYMOUTH

Contents

Illustrations

11 Opinion was divided on the artistic merit of the bridge, but everyone agreed that it was a superb piece of engineering such as Scotland had never before seen

12 1961—the Forth is spanned again, and the two 512-foot towers of the road bridge have already risen from the river

13 End of 1962—the cables are now completed and the first of the decking suspenders are slung from them

between pages 168 and 169

14 Strands of the cable emerge from the anchorage chamber which stretches deep into the earth

15 1962: some 400 feet above the river Forth men work on the catwalk as the spinning wheel carrying the strands of the cable passes overhead

16 By mid-1963 the majesty of the road bridge begins to show, but the railway bridge, now 73 years old, still dominates the Inchgarvie narrows

17 March, 1963, and the suspended structure is slowly extending farther over the Forth

18 Autumn, 1963: the gap in the centre of the bridge is almost closed, and as the men work high above the Firth safety nets are slung underneath to protect them

ACKNOWLEDGEMENTS

Thanks are due to the following for permission to reproduce the photographs in this book: Dunfermline Central Library, from whose prints nos. 1, 2, 3 and 6 were taken; the *Illustrated London News*, 4 and 5; Sir William Arrol & Company, 7, 8, 9 and 10 taken from *The Forth Bridge* by P. Phillips; H. Kelly, South Queensferry, 11 and 18; Consulting Engineers to the Forth Road Bridge Joint Board, Mott, Hay & Anderson with whom are associated Freeman, Fox & Partners, 12, 13, 14, 15 and 17; and John Dewar, 16

Maps

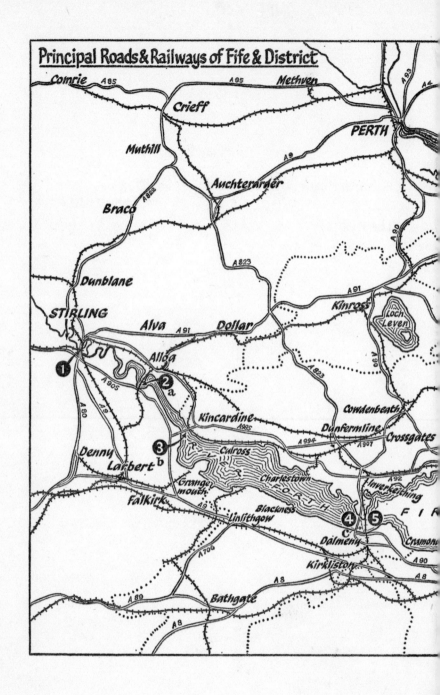

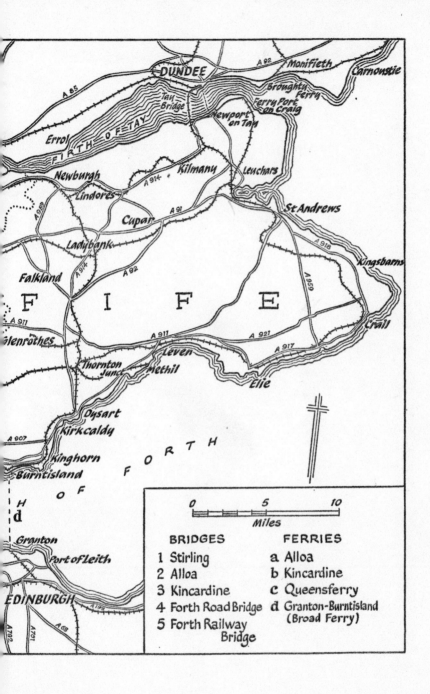

BRIDGES

1 Stirling
2 Alloa
3 Kincardine
4 Forth Road Bridge
5 Forth Railway
          Bridge

FERRIES

a Alloa
b Kincardine
c Queensferry
d Granton-Burntisland
   (Broad Ferry)

To
My MOTHER and FATHER

Preface

MENTION the Forth Railway Bridge to a Scotsman and a note of awe will come into his voice; speak to him of the Forth Road Bridge and he will overflow with pride. That highlights the difference between two ribbons of steel which span the estuary of the River Forth—the railway bridge was built by a few businessmen almost against the wishes of Scotsmen, but the road bridge was built by public opinion. All Scotland takes credit for the great new link between Lothian and Fife, for the entire nation has coaxed, cajoled and pleaded with successive Governments for forty years to have it built.

Now Scotland has its bridge at last, but it is a benefit tinged with sadness, for it ends the life of the ferry which has plied this part of the Forth since times far beyond the Queen's Ferry's eight hundred years of recorded history. Under the Act which provided for the building of the bridge it was laid down that the ferry should cease to operate when the bridge opened. So the ferry must go.

The end of the Queen's Ferry is the end of a story as stirring as any in Scotland's history. It was named after the saintly Margaret who came, as Malcolm Canmore's consort, to lay a civilizing hand on Scotland. It was granted to the monks of Dunfermline by her youngest son, David, and it remained in the possession of the Church until the Reformation. Thereafter the ferry rights were given to landowners who held them for two hundred years until 1809, when they were transferred to trustees.

The Queen's Ferry has had its moments of fortune and moments of misfortune—at one time it would be a great and busy crossing place; at another abandoned.

The ferry will be missed; Scots, and the thousands from all

13

parts of the world who have used it, remember it with affection.

In writing this book I have been helped and encouraged by a great many people. While the bibliography at the end lists published material, I should like to express my thanks for willing assistance given to me by the staffs of many libraries including Register House; The Scottish Central Library; Fife County Library; the public libraries of Edinburgh, Dunfermline, Queensferry, Dundee, Stirling, and Westminster; the Guildhall Library, London; The British Museum; the Newspaper Library, Colindale; and British Transport Commission Archives in London and Edinburgh. Mrs. Nancie Campbell, Reference Librarian at Dunfermline Central Library, and Mr. R. A. Hogg, B.T.C. Archivist in Edinburgh, have been especially helpful and encouraging, and to both of them I would like to express my warmest thanks. Mr. J. McWilliam, Fife County Convener, and officials of A.C.D. Bridge Company Limited, Sir William Arrol and Company Limited, and Messrs. Mott, Hay & Anderson, have also assisted me willingly. I am grateful to all of them.

Once again Alma Player has typed the manuscript, and my wife, Jean Land and John Stocks have assisted with proof reading, and compilation of the index. I am grateful to them, and to my family and friends, for their encouragement as well as their valuable help.

H.D.

London
June 1964

CHAPTER ONE

THE QUEEN'S FERRY

FROM the shore of the Firth of Forth close to the point where Edinburgh now stands, the Romans and succeeding generations of invaders from the south looked across to the gentle hills of Fife, only a few miles away in distance, but beyond their grip. The only way to these inviting lands was by a hazardous crossing of the water, or by travelling far to the west to a place where the river might be forded in safety. When they came to Scotland in the first century A.D. the Romans must have made various thrusts over the Forth and sailed their ships round the coast of Fife, but they never succeeded in bringing the region within their empire.

When they moved northwards it was by way of Stirling and the narrower reaches of the river, but even so the journey was too difficult and communications were too poor for them to be able to hold the northerly parts of Scotland any more securely than they held Fife.

In the steps of the Romans many others took the way to Stirling, so that the township which grew up at that point on the Forth became the focus of all routes to the north, and the strategic key to the Highlands—a position which was enhanced by a castle on a dominant rock, and a bridge over the river. A clue to the importance of this crossing place may be gained from the fact that from Stirling Castle can be seen seven battlefields scattered through five hundred years of Scotland's history—Stirling (1297), Falkirk (1298), Bannockburn (1314), Sauchieburn (1488), Kilsyth (1645), Sheriffmuir (1716), and Falkirk (1746).

Until the middle of the nineteenth century Stirling Bridge was the last to span the river before it reached the sea, some sixty miles away.

On the map this barrier which forced the Romans to make so great a detour looks like a huge arrow pointing into the eastern flank of Scotland. Together with the broad estuary of the River Tay a little farther north, the Forth divides the finest parts of the country, slicing into stretches where fertile soil often overlies mineral wealth. These two estuaries have altered Scotland's history, and retarded the development of some of its richest lands.

Between the two rivers lies Fife, neither apart from Scotland, nor yet a part of it, a county so self-contained that it is generally referred to as the Kingdom. Buchanan described Fife towards the end of the sixteenth century as "a district provided within it own bounds with all things necessary for the use of life".

It had to be, for the Kingdom of Fife was a virtual island.

Fife's slender link with the capital of Scotland was for centuries a series of ferries, the best known of which is the Queen's Ferry. It was here that the Romans must have stood contemplating their advance to the north, for this is the one point at which an easy crossing appears possible, when the water narrows to little more than a mile, and two-thirds of the way across an island rises like a giant stepping-stone. Here the northern shore looks reassuringly near, and the river less menacing. Only when he attempted the journey did man find that this was a piece of deception on the part of the Forth, for squalls and currents can make it treacherous for a small vessel.

Nevertheless, the narrows became a crossing point.

It is not known exactly how early in history that this strip of water came into regular use as a ferry between Fife and the Lothians, but in the seventh century the Pictish king Hungus passed that way after defeating an invader, Athelstane, in battle at a place in East Lothian which thereafter became known as Athelstaneford. We know Hungus crossed the river here, because he paused on Inchgarvie, the island in the estuary, to impale the head of Athelstane on a stake high on the island as a warning to others. There it remained for a long time.

16

For another four hundred years nothing is recorded of the passage across the Forth, but it must have been used frequently, especially when Dunfermline became Malcolm Canmore's capital. Malcolm's consort, Margaret, played an important role in the story of the Forth Passage—perhaps the most important role, for she gave the ferry its name. Margaret came to Malcolm from the sea when her ship was blown on to the Scottish coast in a storm as she was fleeing from England to the Continent in 1069, three years after William of Normandy's conquest.

After her marriage Margaret set about reforming both her husband and her new country, and so successful was she that she is known today as a saintly woman who laid a civilizing hand upon a barbaric nation, who gave Scotland three kings, and who prepared the way for two centuries of peace and progress. Margaret was a devout woman and made many gifts to the church; she encouraged pilgrims to journey to the shrine of St. Andrew in Fife, and as both she and the pilgrims crossed the river at the narrows by Inchgarvie, the passage became known as the Queen's Ferry.

There is no evidence that the name Queen's Ferry had been given to the passage actually during her reign, and in fact Margaret's youngest son, King David I called it "Passagium de Inverkethin". It was only mentioned as the Queen's Ferry in 1164 when Malcolm IV granted to the monks of Scone and their men free passage "ad portum reginae". David I, who had referred to the "Passage of Inverkeithing," handed over the rights of the ferry to the monks of Dunfermline, and that would appear to be how the Church first laid hold on the crossing. In fact David probably granted the rights only to the southern side, for in 1321 King Robert I gave the monks the other shore, which was among lands forfeited by Roger de Moubray for rebelling against the king. At any rate, the Church was in complete control of the Queensferry Passage by the fourteenth century, with its rights confirmed and reaffirmed by monarchs and Popes through the succeeding two-and-a-half centuries until the Reformation.

During the years in which the ferry was under the jurisdiction of the monastery, kings and commoners unrecorded must have passed frequently from Lothian to Fife and back, but only once or twice do we catch a glimpse of these travellers, and then only because some disaster or near disaster befell them. Once when Alexander I was crossing in 1123 a storm caught his ship and wrecked it on the island of Inchcolm, a little farther downstream. A hermit monk gave him shelter, and Alexander expressed his thanks both to God and to his host on the island by founding there an Augustinian monastery.

One hundred-and-sixty-three years on, another Alexander— King Alexander III—made a journey to Fife which is recorded. Life had not used this great Scottish king kindly, and in the space of a few years his wife, his sons, and his daughter all had died, leaving the future of the Scottish crown unsure. To stabilize the succession Alexander married again on 1 November 1285, and one winter's day less than three months later he crossed the Forth on the way from Edinburgh to join his young wife at Kinghorn. It was night by the time he left Inverkeithing to ride on to Kinghorn, and in the darkness his horse stumbled and hurled him over the cliff to his death. This was the tragedy which ended the glorious era begun by Margaret, and threw the nation into centuries of war with England, and dispute and intrigue at home.

At the Reformation the Queensferry Passage became part of the Lordship of Dunfermline, and was bestowed upon Anne of Denmark as a wedding gift by her bridegroom, James VI, in 1589. Soon afterwards the Passage was divided into sixteen parts, four of them fixed to the Ferryhills on the north shore and the remaining twelve to the lands of Muiryhall on the southern one. These sixteen parts were then feued or leased to various individuals whose descendants controlled the Passage for more than two centuries.

With the sixteen shares of the Passage went the right to put boats on the ferry, and also the obligation to keep them in good repair and to provide a safe service for both men and animals. The boats had to be manned by at least six competent hands in fair conditions and by seven "in wyntur and rouche weather". At this time there were no proper landing places, the rocky shore at the Binks, just to the west of South Queensferry harbour, being used on the Lothian side, and possibly the rocks at Haughend on the Fife shore. Piers were not built until the seventeenth century.

From time to time enactments were passed governing the ferry, as in the reign of James VI when ferrymen were forbidden to make the crossing during times of plague in Edinburgh.

The kirk ruled the ferry, too, and in 1635 it was decreed that "whatsoever persons shall break the Sabbath Day by sailing their great or small boats to ply this ferry from the rising of the sun to the twelfth hour of the day, these persones shall be fined for the first fault in twelve shillings Scots the man, and if they shall faill in the same fault any time they shall stand at our Kirk door in sackcloth and make confession of their fault before the congregation. If the masters of the boats be agents to the boatmen they shall pay five pounds."

Enactments, even those of the kirk, could not provide for human nature, and jealousy, smallmindedness and incompetence, all of which prevented the ferry from operating to the best advantage of travellers.

In short, the ferrymen were a troublesome lot. For example George Binks and John Blair were brought before the town's bailies in 1637, and both convicted of injuring each other. Sensibly, the bailies fined each five pounds, the money to be paid by one to the other, and "ye said persons to end in friendshipp and to drink togedder and ye said George Binks to drink first to ye said John Blair in respect he did ye greatest violence to ye said John Blair yan ye said John Blair did to him".

The ferrymen were not altogether popular among travellers either, and in the same year five boatmen were sent to jail for not taking the Lord of Doune across the water.

Charles I thought little of his Scottish subjects, and he saw no reason for changing that opinion when he came north and experienced the Forth crossing in 1633. It was the king's first visit to Scotland since he had left it as a boy of four after his father ascended to the English throne, and in the year of his return he had many matters to worry him. Nevertheless, he found time to complain of the ferries. There were varying accounts of a journey which Charles is reputed to have made from Leith to Inverkeithing—one avers that a boat foundered with the loss of thirty-five of his servants, his silver and household goods, and another that there was a tremendous storm in which eight of his servants perished, while the king himself crossed "in grate jeopardy of his lyffe".

Whichever may be the true version, the fact remains that the king was not pleased with communications in Scotland, and this incident and other similar ones led him to lay charges before the Privy Council accusing the ferrymen of "practices that tended to their owne lucre than to our subjects' good and saftie".

More efforts were made to improve the ferries, and within a few years a new scale of charges was drawn up. It makes odd reading to us today to find that the fare was based on the importance of the passenger and not on the space he would occupy. "Ilk duke, earl or viscount 3s. 4d., ilk lord 1s. 4d., any yr under ye degree for ye man or woman 1d., ilk horse, cow or ox 2d., ilk twenty sheep 4d."

The new regulations did little to better the services, and by 1669 there were so many ships sailing on the Queensferry Passage that the Regality Court decreed "that in all time coming no greater number of boats should ply upon the water at the same time than four, with their yaulls, and no person should be intitled to put up any of these four boats in time coming, but he who by himself and partners should have right to four-sixteenth parts of the water, and who, upon instructing his right in that manner to the court should procure a licence to put up a boat". That clarified the situation—and control was further tightened by another Act the same year, which appointed Justices of the Peace and Sheriffs and their Deputies to supervise the operation of the ferries and to survey and repair them.

Once again the enactment of the law proved easier than its execution, and the last quarter of the seventeenth century saw no great harmony in the operation of the Queen's Ferry. The number of boats in service varied with demand, sometimes being as high as six or seven, and rising to eight in 1689, when there was much movement of troops as William of Orange was consolidating his position following the Glorious Revolution. Clearly some determined regulation of the boats was required, and on two separate occasions this was attempted.

The owners of the sixteen feus of the Passage did not like these extra boats, and pirate ferries were quickly put out of business. Even among themselves there was jealousy and, in the early years of the eighteenth century, quarrelling also. The Laird of Dundas, who feued three thirty-second parts of the Passage and thus was entitled to less than a half share of a boat, applied to the Court of Regality for a licence to operate a ferry and had his application granted. When he put the vessel *George and Alison* into service the other feuars, who included the Earl of Rosebery, applied for an injunction to stop the Laird. To Dundas's claim that there had been eight boats on the ferry in 1689 they replied that this was simply due to the fact that in that year "there was a good deal of Hurry and Stirring, Marches and counter-marches of Troops were frequent".

If the Laird of Dundas was allowed a boat then each of the other heritors ought to be allowed one also, and this would make a total of eleven vessels on the Passage and return the situation to the chaos against which legislation had been attempted for half a century.

"It is submitted to your Lordships," said the feuars in their petition to the Court of Session in Edinburgh, "what Havock it would make on the Passage, what Discouragement it would be to the proprietors if that business which divided amongst four boats, yield a very moderate Gain, were to be divided amongst eleven boats and to subsist their crews".

Although the rights to put ships on the ferry belonged to the feuars of the sixteen parts of the Passage, these men were landowners who did not themselves operate the boats. Instead they let out their right to boatmen who were paid a proportion of the takings. The first sixpence of every pound—each fortieth penny—went to the authorities to provide a fund for the upkeep of the piers. The fortieth penny was known as the Ferry Siller, or Silver. The remainder was divided into four parts, and the first quarter went to the owners of the feus, who were responsible for the upkeep of the boats, and the remaining three-quarters was shared amongst boatmen.

The ferrymen of the Queen's Ferry formed a small, tight-knit community, who claimed the hereditary right to operate the ferry, and guarded their position even more jealously than did the actual owners. By tradition they claimed to have been settled in North Queensferry by Queen Margaret herself, and until the Reformation they were vassals of the monastery of Dunfermline. When Protestantism was adopted by the majority of Scotsmen the boatmen and their families remained loyal to their old faith, so that when Cromwell's soldiers crossed the Forth they were astonished and angry to find a Popish chapel in North Queensferry, and destroyed it. In fact, allegiance to Rome must have been wavering before Cromwell's arrival, for the boatmen had their own loft, with their armorial bearings, in Inverkeithing Parish Church from 1642.

The sailors considered themselves an incorporation although they had no proof of this, and could only defend their claim with another that most other incorporations in Scotland could produce no evidence of their formation either.

The ferrymen not only worked as a community, they lived as one, the earnings from the ferry being divided amongst the entire township. The three-quarters of the takings due to the boatmen after the deduction of the ferry silver was parcelled out into "deals" or shares according to the number of people entitled to a portion. The community then gathered together on a Saturday evening and the "deals" were handed over, one full "deal" to every man who had worked on the boats during the week, no matter whether he had been captain or seaman, or whether he had served in a large ship or a yawl. After the working seamen had received their shares a half "deal" was given to every old man who had formerly been a boatman but was now unfit, and then boys employed on the ferries received a share in proportion to their age, starting with a sixth of a "deal" increasing to a fifth, and so on by a graded scale

until they reached manhood and a full "deal". Widows of boatmen also received some payment, and a sum was finally set
aside to pay for a schoolmaster to teach their children.

The men of North Queensferry did not receive strangers into
their community, and no man born beyond the Ferryhills of
the northern shore of the Passage was permitted to serve as a
sailor. Even the keeper of their inn was a former boatman. On
one occasion a sailor named William Main applied to the Regality Court of Dunfermline and had his name registered as a
ferryman. The boatman allowed him to work on one of the
ships for a full week, but when he came to claim his "deal" on
the Saturday they not only refused to pay him, but bundled
him out of the town.

The rule barring strangers was waived on a few occasions,
however; a blacksmith was brought in at one time, and at the
outbreak of the Napoleonic wars the village could not supply
two men to serve in the Royal Navy as it was required to, so
two outsiders were persuaded to enlist as representatives of North
Queensferry in return for a small payment and the promise that
if they returned safely at the end of the war they would be allowed to join the community with all the privileges of boatmen. Both men did come back, and one became a boatman
entitled to a full "deal", while the other, who had been injured,
received a regular half "deal".

From their youngest day boys of North Queensferry worked
on the boats, and were well acquainted with the tides, rocks,
shores, and currents of the Forth. This training stood them in
good stead to go out into the world as seamen when the small
world of the Ferryhills could no longer contain them. The rewards of the boatman were not high, and while no one was
poor, neither was anyone rich. The more enterprising sought
greater rewards than the weekly "deal" and forsook the ferries
for the Royal Navy and merchant fleet.

As was inevitable there were disputes and jealousies among
the men and women living in so close a community, one quarrel
at the beginning of the eighteenth century being particularly
serious. All this tended to be reflected in the services which
the traveller received on the Passage, but on the whole,

the ferry operated reasonably successfully throughout the latter part of the eighteenth century.

There were complaints, of course, as when a consignment of iron hoops was left lying in the water until they rusted. The hoops had been ordered from Cramond flat mill by a Dunfermline merchant as he passed on his way home from Edinburgh, and the ferrymen were warned to watch out for them and ship them across. The hoops were left lying in the water on the south side of the Passage for one night, and then, when they were transported to the Fife side, they were thrown carelessly on to the rocks below the high water mark and left for four days. By the time the merchant learned that his hoops were awaiting collection at North Queensferry they were "quite overrun with rust" and he submitted a bill for £1 0s. 6½d. for cleaning them.

Passengers and merchants were not the only people who were giving trouble to the boatmen; relations with the owners of the Passage were not at all harmonious, and in fact steadily worsened towards the close of the century.

The owners felt that they were not making enough money out of the ferry, and they decided to let out their quarter share of the takings to anyone who was willing to supply boats for the ferry. An organization called the "boat club" was formed for this purpose and the boat club acquired the right to supply the ferries and draw the owners' money. This scheme still did not satisfy the landowners, and in any case the Napoleonic war had broken out, so they were compelled to drop it.

However, when the war ended—temporarily as it transpired—at the turn of the century they devised another plan to increase their profits by putting their ferry interests up for auction. This brought them much more money, but it did not work, for the men who operated the boats under the new scheme were the ex-naval men from Tyneside, who knew little of the currents of that part of the Forth and as a result were unable to operate regular services and even involved the ferries in a number of accidents.

Furthermore, the seamen of North Queensferry would not admit defeat from the landowners, and obtained an injunction to stop them from selling off the ferry rights. In their appeal to the Lords of Session in Edinburgh the boatmen put forward their story as humble men, emphasizing that much of their history was conjecture because generations of their forebears had been unlettered, simple sailors. They painted a pathetic picture of the hardship that would ensue if the owners were allowed to take over the ferry.

"The whole of the aged and infirm persons of this community," they said, "must instantly become a burden upon the parish, the persons of mature age must scatter themselves over the whole face of the country in search of employment, and now that the Royal Navy is less likely to employ them, they may even be driven beyond the limits of their native country, and lost for ever. It will not be in the power of your Lordships to recall such a set of men from the shores of the St. Lawrence, or the Mississippi, or to bring them back across the Alleghanny Mountains, if they have lost themselves in the wilds of Kentucky. This is not an exaggerated view of the case. If driven from their present employment they must necessarily emigrate somewhere and it is never easy for a poor man to bring back his habitation from any spot in which it is not fixed, and in most cases, impracticable for a sea-faring man to make his family follow him."

Scotland was full of aged and infirm who were a burden on the parish; Scotland was emptying of thousands upon thousands of humble people who could not earn a living in their native country. The threat of being driven to the shores of the St. Lawrence, to the Mississippi, or beyond the Alleghanny Mountains was no fanciful verbiage to blacken the case against the landowners. It was very real.

"Their Lordships" heard the plea of the boatmen, and the owners were stopped in their profit-seeking course. The ferrymen returned to normal, but not for long. The wind of change was already blowing upon the Queensferry Passage, and it was only to take a few years to alter the whole concept of the ferry.

CHAPTER TWO

UNDER OR OVER

THE eighteenth century, its second half in particular, brought great development in communications throughout Scotland, and for an unexpected reason. In 1700 roads were few and poor, with goods transported laboriously on horseback, but then came the Jacobite risings of 1715 and 1745, and the Government embarked upon great road-building schemes to give their troops better access to the Highlands. The task was entrusted to General Wade who, with his men, made some 1,300 miles of roads and more than a thousand bridges.

This burst of road-making did little for Fife, however, being mainly confined to the Highlands and in any case fitting in with military rather than economic needs.

Better roads lay ahead for those south of the Highland Line. Through the Turnpike Acts of the second half of the century hundreds upon hundreds of miles of roads were built by such famous engineers as John Rennie, Charles Macadam and Thomas Telford. These roads were administered by trustees, and were an important part of the industrial growth of Scotland. Wheeled vehicles were for the first time able to travel in safety and relatively swiftly—relatively swiftly, for the coach between Aberdeen and Edinburgh took three days to cover the 120 miles, and the journey from Edinburgh to Glasgow occupied the best part of two uncomfortable days with a night's stay at Harthill.

As the rest of the Lowlands of Scotland struggled to awaken to the Industrial Revolution, so did Fife. Her success may be judged from the comment of a visitor in 1772: "Fertile in soil, abundant in cattle, happy in collieries, in ironstone, lime, and freestone—blest in manufactures; the property remarkably well divided, none insultingly powerful to distress and often depopulate a county—the most of the fortunes of a useful mediocrity".

Yet the Firth of Forth was a barrier to this land of "useful mediocrity", and Dr. Johnson remarked of his arrival there: "Though we were yet in the most populous part of Scotland, and at so small a distance from the capital, we met few passengers."

The reason was not hard to find; the ferries still tended to be irregular, their boatmen were reputedly insolent, and the vessels were moored only on the northern side where the ferrymen lived. Added to that was the problem of uncertain coach services between Edinburgh and Queensferry, through which passengers must have missed the tide frequently and been forced to spend weary hours waiting at the Hawes Inn, anxious to proceed yet powerless to do so.

That was the situation in the opening chapter of *The Antiquary*, and Sir Walter Scott's description has a ring of truth to it.

The Antiquary had waited at the coach office in Edinburgh until his patience was exhausted.

"Woman, is that advertisement thine," he cried . . . "and does it not set forth that, God willing, as you hypocritically express it, the Hawes Fly, or Queensferry Diligence, would set forth today at Twelve o'clock; and is it not, thou falsest of creatures, now a quarter past twelve, and no such fly or diligence to be seen?"

The Antiquary railed on, demanding finally to know if the coach existed at all.

"Oh, dear, yes," replied the harassed woman, "the neighbours ken the diligence weel—green picked out wi' red; three yellow wheels and a black ane." And when this did not satisfy she pleaded: "Oh, man, man, take back your three shillings and mak' me quit o' ye."

The arrival of the coach interrupted this discourse and to

27

the "ineffable pleasure" of the old woman the Antiquary set off. A broken spring and a cast horseshoe delayed the coach further, so that he arrived at the ferry to find that he had missed the tide.

With his travelling companion the Antiquary dined at the Hawes Inn, and crossed the Forth later. He arrived at Fairport —Scott's fictional name for Arbroath—at two o'clock the following day. In twenty-six hours he had covered sixty-seven miles.

The Antiquary was patient—so also was the Rev. William MacRitchie, Minister of Clunie in Perthshire who arrived at North Queensferry with his horse, Cally, at the start of his tour through Britain. He wrote in his diary:

"Breakfast at the ferry. No prospect of a passage till afternoon; contrary winds and heavy rain. No matter, Cally and I must not contend with the winds and the waves. Here let botany afford me some consolation for the delay, and the badness of the weather."

Indeed botany whiled away the time; taking advantage of a fair blink the minister clambered among the rocks above the town and took specimens of flowers. He described the rest of the journey thus:

"Have a quick, rough passage of nine minutes along with some of the King's Black Horse (Major Watson). Arrive in Edinburgh in the evening."

Breakfast in North Queensferry; evening meal in Edinburgh. The Antiquary and the Minister accepted the ferry's shortcomings, but not so the great majority of travellers.

If the Queen's Ferry was bad, the broad ferry, a few miles downstream, was no better. This service ran from Leith and later Newhaven to Burntisland, Kinghorn and the newer harbour of Pettycur.

In 1800 there was no public conveyance of any kind between the Tay and the Forth. and post chaises were kept for hire at Newport, Cupar, Pitlessie, New Inn, Plasterers, and Kirkcaldy. Pinnaces crossed the Forth when the tide was favourable and a crew could be gathered together—circumstances which did not always coincide. At Pettycur it was not unusual for the people to wait two or three days at the inn amusing themselves in drinking or card-playing.

The first public conveyance Fife saw was a two-horse diligence which in 1805 "ran with much deliberation and leisure" between Newport and Pettycur by way of Kennoway, and took the whole day about it.

In 1810, largely by the efforts of the inn-keeper of Cupar, a four-horse coach service was introduced and it was attempted to make the ferries run at all states of the tide. Within a few years the ferry was improving, and was becoming a threat to the Queen's Ferry.

The broad ferry did not escape the censures which were levelled at the Queensferry Passage—with a fair breeze the journey might take about an hour, but in a headwind or calm travellers might spend five or six miserable hours at sea. The small boats used for the passage frequently unnerved passengers, and many must have wished they had never embarked on the ferry before they reached the other shore. Leaving the boat on the Fife side could mean ordeal too, for it involved "walking the plank" of the long gangway which was run down to the water's edge on wheels. In the early part of the century the service between Leith and Kinghorn and Burntisland was operated by sloops manned by only four men, and always known as the "Kinghorn Boat" despite the fact that Pettycur came to be used as a more modern harbour. Generally there were two crossings between Leith and Fife on every tide, though the number increased as the traffic grew. When the regular coach service was introduced, requiring regular sailings of the ferry, an undecked sloop, called the Coach Boat, was put on the broad ferry. At low water it anchored off the harbour and was reached by small skiffs.

The boatmen of the broad ferry enjoyed the same reputation as those of North Queensferry. When Thomas Guthrie, the famous Scottish preacher of the nineteenth century, left his home at Brechin for Edinburgh University in 1815 at the age of twelve, he travelled by way of Dundee and the Tay ferry, crossed Fife on the top of the coach, and covered the last ten miles to Pettycur on foot. It was a wet, stormy night when he

29

arrived at the ferry, and at first the boatmen refused to make the crossing as Guthrie and his tutor were the only passengers. The superintendent of the ferry finally forced them to take the boat out, and as they were leaving the ferry was called back to take on a woman passenger who had just arrived at the harbour. It was an open pinnace, and to add to the discomfort of the cold and rain, the crew bore down on young Guthrie and his tutor, and threatened to pitch them overboard if they did not pay double fare or more. The woman passenger, with a fishwife's tongue, silenced the crew, and Guthrie arrived in Edinburgh safely.

While efforts were being made to improve the broad ferry during the opening years of the century the trustees of the Queen's Ferry and Perth Turnpike Road were not at all pleased at the number of travellers they were losing to the long route by Stirling because of the uncertain Queen's Ferry services.

Meeting at Kinross House on the last day of October 1807, they discussed the inadequacy of the Passage and decided to agitate for a more efficient service. First they asked John Rennie to survey the ferry, and to suggest improvements, and then they persuaded the Chancellor of the Exchequer to pay half the cost of buying the ferry from the hereditary owners and carrying out Rennie's proposals.

An Act of Parliament was passed on 30 May 1809, "nationalizing" the ferry, and the figure for compensation was set by arbitration at £8,673 13s. 10½d.

At the beginning of the nineteenth century the piers were quite inadequate, three in number—two on the south side at Newhalls and Queensferry, and one on the north. Over a period of eleven years following the transfer of the Passage to trustees the improvements suggested by Rennie were carried out, so that the usefulness of the piers was greatly increased.

While the trustees of the Queen's Ferry and Perth Turnpike Road were deliberating what should be done about the Passage another group of gentlemen were considering an alternative improvement to the Great North Road—a tunnel under the Forth. It is said that this idea was not a new one, but at that moment it seemed more propitious then ever—in 1804 work

was begun on a tunnel under the River Thames from Rotherhithe to Limehouse, in the East of London, and the early
success of this aroused interest in tunnelling under the Forth.
In fact, the Rotherhithe Tunnel ran for more than a thousand
feet under the river, almost to the opposite shore, when water
burst in and flooded it. As there was not enough money left to
pump out the works, the tunnel was never completed. However,
in 1804 and 1805 the London excavations were going well,
and surveys were begun at the obvious place for a Forth
Tunnel—Queensferry.

John Grieve, of Edinburgh, gave his opinion on the project
towards the end of 1805. "I have no difficulty in saying that
the thing is very practicable," he wrote. "At Borrowstoneness
they have carried their workings under the same frith for a
mile without experiencing any inconvenience. At Whitehaven
they now work coal for about the same distance under the
Irish Sea, and at both places less water is met with in the workings under the sea than in workings under the land."

Grieve went out and studied the river at the Passage, but was
forced to abandon the narrows at Inchgarvie for two reasons
—whinstone running from the southern shore a large part of
the way across would make tunnelling difficult, and beyond
the shallow shelf at Queensferry the Forth deepened so that the
excavations would have to go very deep to clear the river bed.
Grieve found that this whinstone extended westward to within
half a mile of Rosyth Castle on the north and to Springfield
House on the south bank. West of Rosyth Castle there was
limestone which he also traced across the water, so the tunnel-
lers' hopes lay in that half mile in between.

Travellers may have longed for a tunnel to take them under
the Forth, but the Earl of Hopetoun, one of the local landowners, took a very different view. Because of the earl's objections to making the tunnel entrance so near to Hopetoun
House, Grieve went out six months later, accompanied by William Vazie and James Taylor, and surveyed the ground again.
The others confirmed that the site chosen by him originally
was the best one, but agreed that the entrance to the tunnel
might be carried nearer to Queensferry so that the shaft would

31

curve slowly out, avoiding the earl's land, and meet the original route in midstream.

The earl also complained of the steam engines to be used at the entrances while excavations were in progress, and so the engineers suggested that the one at the Hopetoun end could be dispensed with very soon after work got under way. And lest the earl's aesthetic sense be further offended the surveyors proposed that no special buildings would be needed at the south entrance apart from a toll house and perhaps an inn. Their plans for the northern shore were more ambitious. "A little encouragement with the advantage of a harbour which might be commodiously made at an easy expence, in the bottom of the quarry, might soon produce a busy little town. A neat town at Rosyth, with the castle in its bosom, would not detract from the scenery of Hopetoun House; but if the noble Earl thinks otherwise, he has that in his own power."

The tunnel which Grieve, Vazie and Taylor envisaged could consist of two passages, each 15 feet high and 12 feet wide; with a raised 3-foot pedestrian way in each, or a single tunnel, 24 feet wide and carrying a raised footway in the centre to separate the north and south-bound traffic lanes. The single tunnel was considered preferable.

The cost of this project would be in the region of £160,000, and it would take about four years to complete.

In July 1806, the reports of the three engineers were published, and subscriptions for further preliminary surveys invited. The *Scots Magazine* was enthusiastic about the tunnel which it described as "a work in the highest degree curious and important", but there the matter rested. In the following year another attempt was made to arouse interest in the plan, but thereafter no more was heard of it.

While the tunnel was being discussed hints were thrown out of a plan to bridge the Forth, but this idea met with no more success than did the tunnel. However, one man refused to let the bridge project die; he was James Anderson, a civil engineer in Edinburgh.

Anderson's mind was fired by reports he had read of great bridges in China, some of them several thousand feet long, and one even reputed to stretch three miles. Greatest of all, to Anderson's mind, was that of which he wrote:

"Another bridge constructed of chains in the neighbourhood of King-tung, is described by Duhalde as connecting the tops of two mountains, and thrown over a frightful valley of 750 feet in height, through which the River Laffreny has its course."

This was a time of great expansion in road-making in Scotland, and Thomas Telford, in less spectacular manner, was spanning many rivers.

Inspired by all this, Anderson began in 1817 to make surveys, to take soundings, and to experiment with wood and iron for this bridge of chains across the Forth. It was to be the wonder of the age, far surpassing any other. And like all who had sought an easy way to Fife the focus of his attention became Queensferry.

"The appearance and situation are altogether so favourable and so inviting for some work of art that it has often occurred to the reporter when he considered them attentively, that a bridge of some description ought to be attempted," he wrote.

Anderson planned to cross the river in three giant strides of 1,770 feet, 2,000 feet and 2,000 feet, broken by two pillars, one at the edge of the shelf, where the river deepened, and the other on Inchgarvie island.

Three versions of the bridge of chains were designed, two of them 90 feet above high water level and the third 110 feet above it, the high bridge requiring a fourth span of 1,500 feet over land at its northern end to complete it. The height of the bridge above the water level was important, for Anderson realized that if any interruption of navigation to the ports upstream were threatened his plans would meet fierce opposition.

Anderson made a special journey to Leith Harbour, therefore, and measured a ship of 400 tons with her gallant masts up. The height was 108 feet, leaving just 2 feet of clearance for her to pass under his bridge, but that satisfied Anderson, especially as the same ship could pass through the 90-foot bridge with her top mast up and still have 12 feet to spare. Anderson was confident, therefore, that his bridge was high enough to clear most of the vessels navigating the Forth.

The piers of the bridge soared high and gracefully above the Forth, and appeared most elegant on the plans. In one design, for example, Anderson planned to have cast iron frames on top of the pillars rising 100 feet above the carriageway. Iron lines running from these columns to points at 100-foot intervals on the bridge would support the roadway, and at the same time counteract vibration from wind or weight of traffic.

The breadth of the bridge would be 34 feet, with two pathways, each 4 feet wide, on either side of the carriageway.

Anderson sought the best materials for his bridge—excellent, durable freestone from Well Dean Quarry about a mile from North Queensferry, good quality lime from Elgin Limeworks closeby, oak from the United States of America, and iron from Sweden. To prevent the iron from rusting he proposed to heat it to a certain temperature and dip it in linseed oil before use. This ingenious idea would certainly have saved on paint!

The cost of the simplest of the three designs, one of the 90-foot bridges, was £144,000 allowing £13,442 for "contingencies"; The 110-foot design would be £170,000 and the other 90-foot one, £175,000. Like the tunnel, the bridge would take four years to build.

Whilst shortening the Great Road to the North of Scotland, the bridge would also eliminate the steep and difficult hills into both North and South Queensferry and, more important, it would give the mails uninterrupted passage between Edinburgh and the North.

Anderson expected support from the Queensferry Passage trustees, the trustees of the turnpike roads in the vicinity of the ferry and the General Post Office, as well as from Edinburgh itself, but this was not forthcoming. In fact Edinburgh was too preoccupied with enormous projects for the lighting of the town by gas and the introduction of a supply of pure water to take up Anderson's scheme. Perhaps that was as well, for although the plans looked well on paper an engineer connected with the Forth railway bridge remarked seventy years later that the bridge of chains "was so light a structure that it would hardly have been visible on a dull day, and after a heavy gale it would no longer be seen on a clear day either".

In 1811 the number of passengers on the ferry averaged 228 a day, rising at times to as many as 447. The busiest time of the year was the season of the cattle trysts at Falkirk, where great numbers of animals were driven south and the roads around the ferries were blocked night and day for a week with flocks and herdsmen. These were wild days by the ferry and the boatmen worked at great pressure to cope with the traffic.

Despite the warnings of a retired East India Company sailor, Admiral Sir Philip Durham, that he viewed the matter with a seaman's eye and could tell that a steamboat could never live on the Forth, Leith saw its first steam ship about 1815, and in another five years steamers were sailing regularly to the Forth ports. This new form of power brought an added problem to the trustees of the Queensferry Passage, for the two steamboats, *Tug* and *Dumbarton Castle,* began to call at Kirkcaldy every morning on their way from Leith to Grangemouth, and on the broad ferry ships were sailing not only to Burntisland and Kinghorn, but to Aberdour as well.

With its Highland-bound traffic vanishing swiftly to the Forth steamers, and Fife passengers dwindling also, the Queen's Ferry was in serious trouble, yet the introduction of steam was not merely a matter of buying a boat and announcing a service. The piers, which had been constructed to take sailing boats at all states of the tide, were not suited to ordinary steamers. Yet the committee of management knew that something had to be done.

The committee finally hired a steamship, the *Lady of the Lake,* to try out steam on their narrow strip of water, and they had a model made of a boat specially designed to suit their piers. Satisfied that a steamer would meet their requirements they pledged their sinking fund to raise the £2,369 needed to build one for their service. This vessel was introduced on 1 October 1821, and they named her the *Queen Margaret.*

The new ship operated quite successfully, but in time she became slower as absorption of water increased her draught by six inches. The ferry superintendent, James Scott, persuaded the trustees to lengthen the vessel by eight or ten feet to reduce her draught and increase her speed, and this was done by June 1828.

However, the steamer was a big drain on funds, as is shown by these sample figures for the weekly operation of a Forth steamer about this time:

Engineer	.	.	.	.	£1	10s.	0d.
Skipper	.	.	.	.	£1	5s.	0d.
2 seamen	.	.	.	.	£1	16s.	0d.
Fireman	.	.	.	.		17s.	0d.
Coal average	.	.	.	£5	10s.	0d.
Tallow, oil, rope yarn	.	.	£1	16s.	0d.

£12 14s. 0d.

To meet this extra cost the trustees put away two of their large sailing boats and two pinnaces with their crews.

Although the *Queen Margaret* did not have the speed of the other steamers on the Forth, and the shortness of the passage did not make for ease of operation, she did give the trustees a short respite in their war for passengers. In the ensuing years other steamboats were introduced so that the service was operated by at least three large, primitive steamers and three pinnaces manned by a total crew of thirty-six men and boys.

At the time of the introduction of the *Queen Margaret* the Post Office altered the times of the mails so that instead of passing in daylight throughout the year they had to pass during the night, both northbound and southbound. This required night crews to be kept on both sides of the Firth, in addition to a boat suited to transport mails in all weathers.

Passengers normally boarded the coach at the Hawes Inn on the south side, but this practice was changed to cut delays and the coach was taken along the pier to stand beside the ship. As a result there was an accident in 1838 in which two people lost their lives when the coach fell into the water. The ferryboat had just arrived from Fife, and passengers were boarding the mail coach on Newhalls Pier when the leading horse suddenly wheeled round and coach and horses were thrown into the shallow water. The vehicle landed on its side and two of the occupants were able to thrust their heads through the window and above water until rescued. Two others, a girl and an elderly woman servant, were drowned.

Said *The Scotsman*: "The melancholy result is entirely attributable to the dangerous practice recently introduced of loading the coach on the quay instead of at the inn, as formerly, and at the same time leaving the horses heads unattended."

Leith, the southern terminus of the broad ferry, was a growing, thriving township at the first part of the nineteenth century, and even though its accommodation for shipping was greatly increased still more was needed. In 1818 John Rennie submitted plans for building docks at Newhaven nearby, and although Rennie's plans did not materialize Newhaven did become the port for Forth sailings to such an extent that a new pier, the famous Chain Pier, was built.

The Chain Pier was born into a splendid moment of history when George IV made his famous visit to Edinburgh, an occasion noted for the renaissance of tartan and lavish ceremonial stage-managed by Sir Walter Scott. On landing at the pier the King was met by the greeting strung across the front of an inn in large letters. "Fair fa' your honest sonsie face." leaving unsaid the next line of the quotation from Burns—"Great Chieftain o' the puddin' race."

The Chain Pier was a godsend and it became so thronged that local people called it the baggage pier. Its useful life was short, however, for it was superseded by the new harbour of Granton by the middle of the century. From then on the Chain Pier fell into disuse, and became a place of amusement and a bathing station. It was a sad descent from the great days of the baggage pier. The Chain Pier's end came in a great storm during October 1898; the pier was washed away leaving as its only reminder a public house called the Chain Pier Bar opposite the spot where it stood, and bearing a picture of the pier and the epitaph "Old Chain Pier, erected when King George IV visited Edinburgh. Washed away, October 1898."

The downfall of Newhaven followed the rise of Granton as a port. At the time when the Chain Pier was built there was increasing dissatisfaction over the facilities available to both cargo and passengers bound for and from Edinburgh. A number of schemes were put forward, including one for a new entrance to Leith from the west, another for a harbour at Trinity, and a third for a harbour at Granton which was the idea of Mr. R. W. Hamilton, manager of the General Steam Navigation Company.

The site of Hamilton's harbour was on land belonging to the Buccleuch family, and the proposal was brought to the notice of the Duke of Buccleuch, then aged about thirty. The young duke was enthusiastic about the idea, and, in spite of opposition, had reports and estimates prepared, and called in James Walker, President of the Institution of Civil Engineers, to report on the various schemes mooted for Granton and other harbours. Walker supported the Duke's plan, which was then set before a group of "mercantile and nautical gentlemen" in Edinburgh at a meeting under the chairmanship of Admiral Sir David Milne. Again the plan was approved, so the Duke decided to proceed with the harbour and to foot the bill himself.

A Bill for the opposition scheme at Trinity had been thrown out in 1835, and the Duke's Granton harbour Bill was brought in during the following Session. The Act was obtained in 1837, and work was begun on what is now known as the Middle Pier, the Eastern Breakwater and Western Pier which protect it being added later in the century. Stone for the pier was brought from the Duke's own quarries close by, timber from Memel, gas from Leith, and water straight from Corstorphine Hill to contribute to the great project.

The first part of the pier was completed in time to be opened on Queen Victoria's Coronation Day, 28 June 1838, and of course it was named Victoria Jetty in her honour. The opening ceremony was performed by the Duke's brother, Lord John Scott.

Edinburgh was tremendously impressed with both the harbour, and the road leading to it from Inverleith. Both were held to be the finest in Scotland, and soon after the opening of the Victoria Jetty a correspondent wrote to *The Times*:

"On Wednesday last I drove down to Granton Pier, accompanied by some friends, whose intention it was to proceed on the *Monarch* steamship for London. I had repeatedly heard of this stupendous undertaking, its eligible situation, the facilities it offered for the accommodation of passengers, goods, horses and carriages, embarking and disembarking, and the depth of water affording vessels at all times of the tide to approach it without danger, thereby avoiding that great inconvenience formerly experienced by passengers by the hazardous employment of small boats.

"On my arrival at the pier, I found that the reports circulated respecting it had not been exaggerated; on the contrary, it far exceeded my expectations. The beauty of the day and the attraction of the pier had drawn a numerous assemblage of persons together, to witness the departure of their friends; the scene on proceeding along, was stimulating and busy, crowds of carriages and other vehicles driving down, wagons discharging their goods, with a rapidity truly astonishing, together with 100 or 200 workmen actively engaged in an opposite direction, erecting further accommodation.

"Can sufficient praise be bestowed on the noble founder of this great work, which, in a commercial point of view, will not only immortalize his name, but be the means of increasing to a great extent the trade of Edinburgh and its vicinity?

"The whole seemed to be conducted with the greatest order and regularity, and that intolerable nuisance of porters, coachmen, cabmen, and other vagrants was altogether avoided."

The Duke's pier received the accolade in 1842 when it was chosen as the landing place for the Queen and Prince Consort on their first visit to Scotland after the Queen's accession. Every vantage point was taken long before the Queen was due to land and the Duke of Buccleuch arrived at midnight the night before to be ready to receive the royal party in the morning. At three o'clock he was joined by the Prime Minister, Sir Robert Peel. The royal yacht, *Royal George*, had anchored for the night in Aberlady Bay, and first thing in the morning she proceeded to Granton where the Queen disembarked at 8.55. The royal arrival took Edinburgh Town Council by surprise and Members rushed from their beds, their festive boards, and even from behind their shop counters to receive the royal couple. The indignity of the councillors' rush must have made a smile play on the lips of the magistrates of Leith who were up early enough to receive the visitors.

After fifteen days' triumphal tour of Scotland the Queen and Prince Albert departed from Granton in the General Steam Navigation Company ship, *Trident*. Granton had come through its first moment of glory.

Slowly the pier extended seawards in 1843, but bad weather caused delays so that it was not completed until October of the following year. Nevertheless it was a splendid piece of work— 1,700 feet long and providing berths for no fewer than 10 steamers, some of them as large as 1,000 tons.

The correspondent of *The Times* commended the absence of vagrants, but perhaps a vagrant should have the last word on the great new harbour. The pier was a sight not to be missed, and Edinburgh folk flocked to view it. In the end the Duke, seeing a small, but not to be scorned source of revenue in this curiosity, levied a twopenny toll on all pedestrians using his pier.

It was related that shortly afterwards a man was accosted by a beggar soon after paying his twopence. "No, I have just given my last penny to the Duke of Buccleuch," he protested.

"Ah," replied the beggar, "is he upon the tramp, too?"

CHAPTER THREE

RIGHT OF WAY THROUGH FIFE

HAVING found in her new roadways a wonderful means of transporting the materials essential to her industrial nascence, Scotland soon discovered another—the railway. As in England the first lines were wagonways for transit of goods, principally coal, and before "real" steam-powered railways arrived several of these primitive lines existed in Scotland: among the most famous the Halbeath Tramway in Fife, and the Duke of Portland's line from Kilmarnock to Troon on the Ayrshire coast, which was opened in 1810 to carry coals from the Duke's mines to the sea. The trucks were horsedrawn, but as a means of transport the tramways were relatively fast, and manufacturer and traveller alike soon came to appreciate their value as a new means of locomotion. The lines were even used for pleasure trips—the Duke of Portland's Railway, for example, taking miners on excursions to the seaside.

Scotland did not lag behind in the building of genuine railways—her first was opened only a year after the famous Stockton and Darlington Railway, and ran from Monkland to Kirkintilloch, a distance of ten miles between collieries and the Forth and Clyde Canal. As with the primitive tramways, the Monkland line was designed to carry goods, but as with the others also, it was soon adopted for passenger travel.

By the time the Victorian era began there were ambitious plans for railways in Scotland. The English companies were scheming to cross the Border, and lines were sought in several parts of the country, particularly to link Glasgow with Edinburgh, and Glasgow with Paisley and the Ayrshire coast. The Edinburgh and Glasgow Railway was on the verge of being sanctioned in 1837 when William IV died and Parliament was dissolved. It took another year for the Act to be obtained, and the railway was opened on 21 February 1842. The line ran forty-six miles from Queen Street in Glasgow, to Haymarket in Edinburgh.

In the east of Scotland interest in the new railways was not lagging—they were being planned, applied for, and even built. Here, too, there had been a horse-drawn and much ridiculed line graced with the splendid name of the Edinburgh and Dalkeith Railway. Comic the line may have been, but it was an important pioneer in the east of Scotland.

As in the west these railways were sought primarily for the transportation of goods, and it was inevitable that thoughts should turn to linking the centre of Edinburgh with the ports of the Forth so that goods could be shipped easily to the markets of the capital. Such a line was devised to take advantage of the expanding harbours of Leith and Newhaven, and of the projected harbour at Trinity. The name defined the route—Edinburgh, Leith and Newhaven Railway. The idea was to start from Canal Street, Edinburgh, where Waverley market stands today, and run underground across Princes Street, by the line of South St. Andrew Street, the east side of St. Andrew Square, Duke Street, Dublin Street, and Drummond Place to Scotland Street, where it would emerge. From there it would travel on by Canonmills to Trinity and Newhaven, and a branch would follow the Water of Leith to Leith.

A committee of management was duly set up, and an Act of Parliament was applied for in 1835. With the backing of all the local Members of Parliament the Bill quickly received its First and Second Readings, and "went triumphantly through Committee", but then delays began, and opposition was marshalled. Dr. Patrick Neill, printer of the *Encyclopaedia Britannica*, objected to the line which threatened his property, and hurried south to London to press his case. Throughout the building of the railway Dr. Neill was its enemy, even issuing pamphlets against it.

42

Nor was Neill the only objector; the Government refused to sanction the tunnel which passed under the Custom House in Drummond Place unless the company bought the entire property. Eventually a compromise was agreed to so that the railway need only buy if the property were damaged.

These objections merely delayed the Bill; it was the chairman of the Lords Committee who slew it by altering monetary clauses. Under the rules of the House this was not permissible, and so the Bill had to be thrown out and reintroduced the following year. This time it was successful.

In April 1836, when the Bill was on its successful passage through Parliament, the company's shares reached the highest premium of any railway shares in the United Kingdom in proportion to the deposit paid. Enemies did not fail to point out that some directors took advantage of this situation to sell out.

As in many instances in the future the obtaining of an Act and formation of a company were the simplest parts of building a railway. In the case of the Edinburgh, Leith and Newhaven it took seven years, and many quarrels, and extensive curtailment of the scheme before a train passed over the line.

"Probably there is no instance on record of a railway company having encountered so many difficulties as the Edinburgh, Leith and Newhaven Company and living," commented the *Railway Record* after the first part of the line was opened.

Work was begun in 1837, and at two o'clock on the afternoon of Monday, 7 May, the following year a little ceremony was held at the Chain Pier to mark the laying of the foundation stone of the Newhaven terminus. Although the day was fine the turnout of spectators was disappointing, largely because the company had not made it widely known that the event was to take place. Nevertheless, those present were in good spirits and drank a bumper to the project, while the workmen made do with a plentiful supply of Greig's best March ale and biscuits, "which they seemed to relish with much good humour and glee".

After laying the stone Mr. James French told the assembly: "The citizens of Edinburgh are still unaware of the unique

43

advantages this undertaking will be to them; and I have no hesitation in saying that the reduction of the price of fuel will be a saving to our city and Leith of not less than £50,000 per annum for the coals brought to these places by steam and this railway".

"I sincerely hope," he went on after waxing enthusiastical on the project, "that this day twelvemonths we will have the pleasure of opening the line to the depot at the foot of Scotland Street."

Indeed many citizens of Edinburgh were not aware of the advantages of the Newhaven line; nor were many of the shareholders who soon regretted their agreement to sink capital into the project.

The following twelvemonth and the one after that as well saw many wild claims for compensation from the owners of property through which the railway was to pass. At Trinity between £30,000 and £40,000 was demanded and £4,250 awarded after a court battle; for land at Heriot Hill between £7,000 and £10,000 was sought, but the court fixed the figure at £3,250; and the Governors of George Heriot's Hospital, who asked for £7,000 to £9,000, had to accept only £2,500.

The Newhaven Railway met with nearly as much trouble from its proprietors as from the landowners of Edinburgh and Leith. When calls were made on the shares for which they had subscribed a number refused to pay, and the company had to go to court time after time to enforce payment.

Among the reluctant subscribers was a Liverpool stockbroker called Richard Dawson, and when the company took Dawson to court early in 1839, he retaliated by publishing a vicious attack on the board of directors. So successful was Dawson that he was able to turn up in Edinburgh seven months later, armed with enough proxies to address to the proprietors "some observation as to the qualifications necessary for directors", and then to tailor the board to his own liking. Thereafter he became the railway's ardent supporter and its agent in Liverpool, and, using the same lawyers as had defended Dawson, the railway company continued to sue others who were in arrear.

As a result of the procrastination and obstinacy of the proprietors work on the line was at a standstill by the end of 1839.
Funds were exhausted and there was little hope of completion.
However, Dawson and his legal men got things moving so
successfully that the board were able to report the following
summer that, although a number of shareholders were still
not responding to calls, the amount recovered on old calls
through court action had enabled them to resume work on the
line. Financial depression continued in Britain, and the resulting bankruptcies did not make the task of Dawson or the
board any easier.

In view of the fact that estimates for the line had proved
wildly wrong, the Company went back to Parliament for powers
to abandon the Leith branch and to take the line only to Trinity
instead of to Newhaven. It also decided to leave the building of the Scotland Street tunnel until the first part of the railway was opened.

A writer to the *Railway Times*, stung by this curtailment,
stormed that there was no such railway under construction as
the name implied, and one must admit it does seem odd for a
railway named the Edinburgh, Leith and Newhaven to run only
from the outskirts of the former to neither of the latter places.
With accuracy another correspondent called it the oyster railway, because it had neither head nor tail.

In the *Railway Times* discontented shareholders and trouble-
makers found a lusty voice. Nothing the railway company did
was right, and every circular issued by Dawson—and they were
many—was torn apart with the maximum of malice. Fraud
and falsehood were alleged in language which today would
fill the Court of Session with libel suits, and no opportunity
was missed to denounce the company. Oddly, a great deal of
this storm centred on Liverpool, where many shareholders
lived—no doubt a result of Dawson's enthusiastic advocacy
of the project—and the *Liverpool Standard* carried many
favourable reports of the line. Eventually the feud developed
into a battle between the *Liverpool Standard* and the *Railway
Times*. Even when the Newhaven Railway began to prosper
the *Railway Times* refused to say a word in its favour. Com-

mented another railway journal: "It has been the fate of the Edinburgh, Leith and Newhaven Railway to have been under the clouds, and very lately our contemporary, for reasons best known to himself, has visited it with the utmost venom of his vituperation, mingled we are informed with no little of atrabilious invention".

In January 1840 the opening of the line was forecast for September, and four months later the date was put back to May of the following year. But instead of completion, 1841 saw a new crisis on the directors' hands. The *Railway Times* zealously reported the dissatisfaction of the shareholders, and often added its own opinions.

Of the directors' report issued in the summer of 1841 it commented, with customary dusting of exclamation marks and italics:

"The only account it contains of receipts and payments consists of two solitary items, namely:

Received since last report . .	£9,583 13s.	9d.
Expended since last report .	£11,049 3s.	7½d.

"This is 'cool' certainly! From what *sources* the first item has been received, or in what *manner* the second item has been expended no particulars are given, and for anything that appears to the contrary, the one might have been derived *from the sale of the shareholders' own land and houses*, and the other might have been squandered *uselessly and lavishly*. At all events no information is given on these points which are of vital importance.

"In their previous report the Directors gave a pledge that this line 'of one mile and a quarter' *(which has now been upwards of five years in progress)* should be completed at the latest by the 1st of May last: and yet the works are at this moment as unfinished as before!

"The Directors have *now* (!) settled the terms on which they are to obtain possession of the remaining property, but what those terms are, or what the cost will be they most carefully conceal as though *that* were not the business of the proprietors.

"They state that £24,000 more will be required to finish their 'mile and a quarter' railway—that of this sum £10,453, will be raised by calls in arrear (but which none but themselves affect to believe will be forthcoming) and that the deficiency will be supplied by selling out the forefeited shares at *£10 discount*! Now it is well known that the shares with the *full amount* paid up are unsaleable at any price, and that no man in his senses would take them at £10 discount. In fact we are credibly informed that they have long since been hawked about without finding a purchaser *for 5s. apiece*, with £19 per share paid up."

The journal went on to say that the object seemed to be to conceal what ought to be known, "thus leaving this wretched concern involved in far greater mystery and obscurity as to the real state of its affairs, than before."

This time the *Railway Times* was right in its fears, and the public had only a month to wait before the directors announced that the position was so serious that unless immediate assistance was forthcoming they would have to stop work on the line altogether. They confirmed that the sum required to complete the Scotland Street–Trinity portion was £24,000, and admitted that at that moment they had scarcely enough to pay their bills for the current month.

To show the potential of the line the board had a traffic survey carried out, and sent its secretary to London and Liverpool to seek support. Dawson was still the railway's advocate in Liverpool, and the search for more capital gave the *Railway Times* another opportunity to attack him. Maliciously it recited the history of the concern, the facts, it claimed, emanating from "a highly intelligent English shareholder"—and when Dawson issued a new circular the journal compared the facts it contained with his attack in 1839 when he had been sued for non-payment of calls:

1839:   One point of the plan is all but impracticable, and the estimate for land and houses does not amount to one third of the actual cost of the land alone. The original estimate for the railroad was £100,000 which was to complete the entire line from Edinburgh to Leith via

47

Trinity and Newhaven; and though £40,000 will be saved on the new line by the tunnels and excavations, the sum of £100,000 will still be required to carry the line to Trinity alone.

1841: Our little but valuable concern will be completed, notwithstanding all the difficulties we have had to encounter, for the estimate as laid before Parliament. This circumstance is almost unparalleled in railway concerns.

1839: The original Chairman of the company held fifty shares, but never paid even the Parliamentary deposit! The Vice-Chairman holds twenty-five shares, but not having latterly paid his calls! the directors are proceeding against him for the same.

1841: The bold and manly declarations made by the directors, who are all men of high honour and probity.

1839: The company were very unfortunate in the plans of their Engineers (Messrs. Grainger and Miller)—and also in the estimates of the property required to be bought. The great difference in the estimates is understood to be in the valuation of the land, and in consequence of the engineers having adopted some erroneous data.

1841: On careful examination of the scale of traffic, which has been prepared by that respectable and experienced Engineer, Mr. Grainger, and may with confidence be relied on.

Ignoring the attacks Dawson concentrated on keeping the company alive. With the Edinburgh and Glasgow Railway nearing completion, hopes were buoyed for a junction to that line, and enough money was raised for work to continue. The following summer the railway was finished, and the committee set up to arrange its opening showed commendable opportunism in choosing the 1 September, the day of Queen Victoria's arrival at Granton. With all of Edinburgh thronging to Granton in holiday mood, their railway was assured of a large quota of passengers, and even the tardy Edinburgh magistrates may have found the railway convenient to speed them towards Granton in their undignified rush to be there on time.

The *Railway Times* remained churlishly silent on the success of the railway. It did, however, publish a letter some months later over the signature "Solomon", which said, "Although I am aware that the concern is no favourite of yours, yet perhaps you will so far befriend the shareholders as to inquire what the directors are about. Some rumours were afloat that the railway was ready for the locomotives at the time of the Queen's visit, but since that time we have heard nothing whatever of it; even Mr. Dawson has been utterly mute. Be kind enough, sir, to inquire for us whether the railway has been lost or not because, if such should be the case, the directors were at least bound to advertise it."

What were the directors about? For one thing they were hard at work turning their project from what the *Railway Times* in a more polite moment had called "one of the hollowest bubbles ever blown", into a valuable little railway holding the key to the North of Scotland.

It was now apparent that Trinity harbour would not be built, and the Duke of Buccleuch's pier at Granton was nearing completion, so the Newhaven company decided to carry its line on to Granton. On learning that the Edinburgh and Glasgow had decided to extend from Haymarket to Princes Street the Newhaven Railway went ahead with its Scotland Street tunnel and applied for a Granton Extension Act. However, the Edinburgh and Glasgow dropped the Princes Street scheme and the Newhaven board, feeling let down, shelved its plans too. In 1844, both companies agreed to proceed at last and this time there were no hitches. By the Act for the Granton extension powers were also obtained to build a Leith branch, and to alter the railway's name to the Edinburgh, Leith and Granton Railway.

Work on the Scotland Street tunnel went well, and apart from a short scare for the foundations of houses in Scotland Street and a flooding accident in which four workmen died, there were no major mishaps. In its day the tunnel was considered a most remarkable piece of engineering work, only a little less marvellous than Brunel's Thames Tunnel which had just been opened. The tunnel sloped away from Princes Street at a gradient of nearly 1 in 27 and at first it was decided to use smokeless engines in it, but this idea was later abandoned for the more economical method of an endless rope worked by a stationary engine. Locomotives were attached at Scotland Street to take the trains on to Granton. At the Princes Street end space was at a minimum and access to the station was from Canal Street or by a flight of stairs from Princes Street, just opposite the foot of South St. Andrew Street. Horses were used to haul the carriages into position for the rope to be attached.

The building of the tunnel was delayed and before it came into service there were recriminations and accusations against the contractors for not speeding the work. In fact the Granton and Leith lines, not even sanctioned when the tunnel was begun, came into use before it.

The Edinburgh, Leith and Granton was now well on its way from the heart of Edinburgh to the Firth of Forth, and as if to prove its growing strength, the little railway took on two comparative giants, the North British and the Edinburgh and Glasgow who were planning to grab its station territory at Princes Street, squeezing it from opposite directions like an almond in a nutcracker. The Edinburgh, Leith and Granton resisted and, while the two companies obtained station space, they did not push it out altogether.

Its station secured, the company continued with the tunnel and Leith and Granton extensions. The surface lines were opened in 1846 and the tunnel the following year, so that, with the exception of a few yards over which they had still not settled terms with the Duke of Buccleuch, the Granton line had reached the Forth ferry.

The next big jump was to the other side of the firth and to the north, and as these were the times of the Railway Mania, there had already been a pretty piece of jostling to secure lines in Fife.

Up to 1844 railways had by-passed the county, and tended to take the roundabout route by Stirling and Perth. Then came the railway mania years, and schemes galore.

There were two obvious starting-off points for railways through Fife—Queensferry and Burntisland, and both were eagerly sought by companies named respectively the Edinburgh and Perth by Queensferry and the Edinburgh and Northern. For some years before either began seriously to contend for the right of way through Fife there had been talk of building a railway to Perth and Dundee, and surveys had been made.

In April 1844, a prospectus was issued for the railway from Burntisland to Perth and to the Tay at a point opposite Dundee. The capital was to be £800,000 exclusive of rolling stock and plant. The railway planned to cross the Tay by a ferry opposite Dundee, whose history was as ancient as that of the Queen's Ferry, but it was soon discovered that there would be trouble over the ferry rights, so the project was recast to include a bridge over the Tay. To limit the cost of this huge scheme single line track was to be laid for most of the way.

This Edinburgh and Northern Railway was essentially a local line, much of its capital emanating from Fife, the surrounding counties and Edinburgh, rather than from the other side of the Border. In the opinion of the *Railway Times* this was not altogether an advantage, for it gave as its editorial opinion that the lack of English capital deprived the Northern of "business talents, the straightforwardness, and the freedom from local and personal prejudices of Englishmen".

The opposing scheme in its original form was for a line from the Edinburgh and Glasgow Railway at Gogar, just outside Edinburgh, to South Queensferry, and then from North Queensferry by Cowdenbeath, the east side of Loch Leven and Glenfarg to Perth. There would be branches to Dunfermline and Kirkcaldy, the latter serving the Lochgelly coalfield. The promoters later added to their plan a line from Cowdenbeath by the west of Loch Leven, to join the original railway beyond Kinross, and for a while they could not decide whether to promote both of these schemes or only one. The Edinburgh and Perth Railway was not ready to set its project before Parliament in 1845, but when the Northern applied for its Act in that year the Queensferry company was its fiercest opponent with two main aims—to keep the Northern out of Perth and the Lochgelly coalfields.

Describing the Parliamentary battle the Chairman of the Northern said later that on entering the Committee Room of the Commons the scene was most appalling—the army of counsel, peers, admirals, and other opponents being so great that the promoters of the scheme were crushed into a corner.

The Admiralty fought the Tay bridge plan on the grounds that it might impede navigation, so the promoters abandoned the bridge and the final portion of the line from Cupar to the Tay. This would leave them free to return in another Session and apply for an extension to any point on the Tay which they might choose. Mutilated as the scheme now was, the Northern succeeded in proving that it could muster sufficient traffic to make the line worthwhile, and after seventeen days of argument, with thirty-three witnesses appearing for the scheme and thirty-eight against it, the Preamble of the Bill was proved and it was allowed to proceed. Once through the Commons the Bill met renewed opposition in the Lords, and the end of the Session was now so near that there was a danger of time running out before it could be passed. In desperation a bargain was struck with the rival Queensferry Company; by this the Northern Bill was to be allowed to go through on condition that its promoters would not fight the Bill for the Edinburgh and Perth's main line to Perth or its branch to meet the Northern at Thornton in the next Session. The price of the companies was the concession of the Lochgelly coalfields to the Queensferry Company, and the only hope of the Northern lay in the stipulation that it would be allowed to deposit plans for a similar branch from Thornton to Dunfermline in case the Perth company's Bill failed.

Thus the Northern obtained its railway to Perth and Cupar, but it had to make a double line of rails instead of single, and for this was allowed to increase its capital. The next Session of Parliament would prove whether the price paid for the Act had been too high.

The end of 1845 brought the peak in Fife's own railway mania, with no fewer than sixteen schemes lodged with the Sheriff Clerk of the county. The Edinburgh and Perth, together with the Glasgow and Dundee Junction, sliced through the county and constituted a sore threat to the Northern, and in addition the situation was further complicated by other schemes such as that from Newburgh to meet the Scottish

Central near Perth, the Perth and Dundee, a high level bridge over the Tay to connect it with the Edinburgh and Perth, and the purchase of the Newport ferry by Glasgow and Dundee Junction interests.

By 1846 the Edinburgh and Perth had obtained an agreement for the Edinburgh and Glasgow to build the line south of the Forth and was endeavouring to obtain the Queensferry rights which it considered essential, so it went ahead and petitioned Parliament for leave to introduce a Bill for the line by the west side of Loch Leven and Kinross to Perth, and for the branches to Dunfermline and Thornton. The plans were badly made and did not pass Standing Orders, so the Bill was thrown out. The Northern seized its chance and, with the traders of Dunfermline standing open-armed to welcome it, quickly had its branch from Thornton sanctioned.

Elsewhere in Fife the Northern was manœuvring skilfully and successfully. The Admiralty still opposed the bridge over the Tay, and the Newport Ferry was clearly lost, so the company decided to turn instead to Ferryport-on-Craig, later known as Tayport, and to obtain the ferry rights there. It would then only take an agreement with the Dundee and Arbroath Railway to ensure transit of passengers the last few miles from Broughty Ferry into Dundee and to the north-east of Scotland.

This decision made another important change possible—it was no longer necessary to run the Perth branch along the edge of the River Tay, which would be a costly line to make; instead, it could be deviated through Strathearn, where an opposition project was under way. By taking over this Strathearn line's interests the Northern eliminated opposition in that corner of the county, and made sure of its route from Ladybank to meet the Scottish Central Railway at Hilton just outside Perth. The last few miles into the city would be on Scottish Central line.

Bills for branches from Kirkcaldy to Lochgelly and from Leslie to Markinch were both lost, and another for a line from Ladybank to Kinross was abandoned immediately it had served its purpose and helped to defeat the Glasgow and Dundee Junction and Edinburgh and Perth schemes.

That was typical of the complicated scheming and manœuvring that went on not only in Fife, but throughout Britain in the mania years. Tens upon tens of thousands of pounds were squandered on worthless and wasteful lines, many of them proposed only to thwart another's plans, and then abandoned as soon as they had served their purpose.

The Northern was now in a position to proceed with the purchase of the Ferryport-on-Craig ferry to make an agreement from the Dundee and Arbroath Railway to carry its traffic from Broughty Ferry. Both of these plans went smoothly, thus securing for the Northern its Tay crossing.

All the while the Northern had not forgotten the Forth, where the Granton pier was completed, and the larger companies were angling to secure traffic north from Edinburgh. Here the little Edinburgh, Leith and Granton line was pawn in the game of chess for the route north.

All its life the Granton company had sought a junction with the Edinburgh and Glasgow; indeed in the lean years of the late 1830's that had been almost the only hope the directors could offer to shareholders. Then in 1842 there had been the unfortunate incident of the two agreeing to carry out their extensions to Princes Street and Granton in unison, but the Granton company had been let down by the decision of the Edinburgh and Glasgow not to proceed. Again in 1844 they sought Parliamentary sanction for the extensions, and the Bills of the two railways were considered so much one plan that they were referred to the same Commons Committee and reported on accordingly. Suddenly the Edinburgh and Glasgow renegued and sponsored a line to Granton by the west side of Edinburgh, and at the same time the Edinburgh and Leith Atmospheric line was projected—as the Granton company chairman put it —"if not under the auspices at least with the sanction of several Edinburgh and Glasgow directors".

Two other opposition lines to the Forth appeared at about this time—one by the Caledonian on the west side of the capital and another called the Edinburgh and Leith Direct on the east. Leith's own railway mania jeopardized the precarious little Granton company just at the moment when it looked like thriving at last.

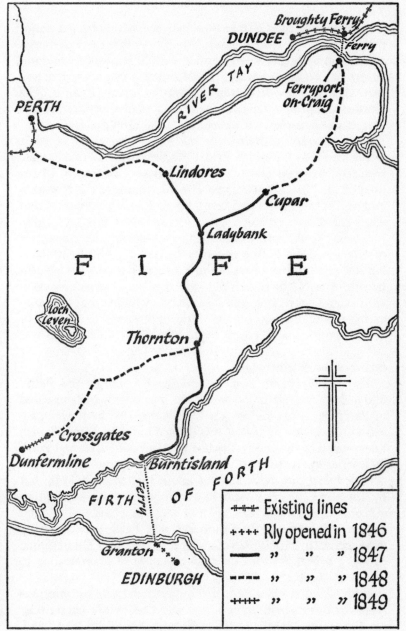

The Railways of Fife, 1845-9

Nevertheless the Granton line had one advantage—a major portion of it was already built. Mindful of that the Edinburgh and Glasgow sought amalgamation with it, but terms could not be agreed. Towards the end of 1845 came a last approach, and thereafter silence—from the Glasgow company, that is. The Northern Railway stepped in and in a matter of months had agreed in principle to a merger with the Granton Railway.

Parliamentary authority for the union was given in 1847, but before then the North British Railway tried to amalgamate with the Northern and was rejected. John Learmonth, Chairman of the North British, was also Chairman of the Northern and of the Edinburgh and Glasgow, and so it was natural that when the North British looked for an outlet north of Edinburgh he should turn to his Northern company. A committee of directors from both companies was set up, with Learmonth himself as a representative of the Northern but not of the North British. The North British felt sure that the Queensferry company would get its line, and insisted on including that company in the amalgamation, but the Northern would have none of this. Negotiations therefore broke down, and Learmonth was left in such an equivocal position that he had to resign from the board of the Northern.

The North British now backed the Edinburgh and Perth, and in 1847 the Perth company's Bill was once again presented to Parliament. The defeat was humiliating—without even calling an opposition witness it was thrown out. The North British knew this was the end of the line for the Edinburgh and Perth and withdrew its support. In fact the Perth promoters did not accept defeat and reformed for another attempt in 1848, but by this time the Northern had consolidated its position so successfully that the Bill did not stand a chance. The final nail in the coffin of the Edinburgh and Perth was an agreement between the Northern and the Stirling and Dunfermline to carry a branch from their joint station at Dunfermline to North Queensferry.

With Granton's new pier affording better facilities, improvements to Burntisland harbour had also been put in hand under an Act of 1842 by the Duke of Buccleuch and Sir John Gladstone, father of William Ewart Gladstone. Sir John, who was an important shareholder in the Edinburgh and Northern company, and the Duke had the ferry rights between Pettycur and Aberdour. The harbour of Burntisland and the ferry between the two ports were later bought by the Edinburgh and Northern Railway to complete its route.

The actual building of the railway went ahead despite all the jockeying of the mania years. In 1846, the first ground was broken at Kinghorn, and on Tuesday, 31 August 1847, a group of directors travelled over the line from Burntisland to Cupar, where they were entertained by the Provost. On Friday, 9 September, the Government inspector examined the railway and passed it for opening, and at the end of the following week six hundred ladies and gentlemen entrained at Burntisland and travelled to Cupar where a magnificent banquet was set out in an elegant pavilion erected for the occasion. On the next Monday the first passengers travelled between Edinburgh and Cupar and Edinburgh and Lindores. From the two terminal stations coaches took passengers on to the Dundee ferry and to Perth. The time from Edinburgh to Cupar and Lindores was two and a quarter hours, and to Perth and Dundee a little over four hours.

On 17 May 1848 the line reached Ferryport-on-Craig, and by July it had connected with the Scottish Central outside Perth.

The Edinburgh and Northern had won the route through Fife to the north. It was a victory that boded no good for the ancient ferry at the Inchgarvie narrows.

CHAPTER FOUR

THE FLOATING RAILWAY

THE Edinburgh and Northern Railway changed its name to the Edinburgh, Perth and Dundee Railway in 1849. With lines to St. Andrews and other parts of Fife being added the Kingdom was soon remarkably well connected to Edinburgh, although there were exceptions. Dunfermline, for example, lay only sixteen miles north-west of the capital, but was thirty-seven miles away by rail.

Communication was good, yet there was a danger that the inconvenience of the double ferry crossing might drive goods and passengers bound for destinations north of Fife to the longer but more comfortable route by Stirling. At this moment the railway recruited as its engineer a young man of twenty-seven whose ideas were as large and bold as the mighty Victorian age in which he lived. His name was Thomas Bouch.

Bouch was born at Thursby, in Cumberland, the third son of a sea captain, William Bouch, and it is said that a lecture by his teacher on the Raising of Water in Ancient and Modern Times made such an impression on Thomas that he began to read books on mechanics, and set his heart on a career in engineering. On leaving school Bouch joined a mechanical engineer in Liverpool, and at the age of seventeen he had his first taste of railway engineering on the construction of the Lancaster and Carlisle Railway. Five years later he became one of the resident engineers of the Stockton and Darlington Railway. Although Bouch's knowledge of his subject was suspect and he was reputed to have a knack of adopting and adapting the ideas of others, he was now making his name as an engineer.

In January 1849 Bouch left England to become Manager and Engineer of the Northern just before its name was changed to the Edinburgh, Perth and Dundee. At that time many people considered it unlikely that the time of the ferry journey could be cut, and in fact in his *Tullis's Guide to the Edinburgh and Northern Railway* in 1848, James Bruce had written: "Without running the risk of involving ourselves in the presumption of those who take upon them to set boundaries and limits to the possible achievements of science, it may be admitted that, in all likelihood, for many years to come, no very considerable improvements can be effected in the rate of quickness at which the railway's boats are now taken across the ferries".

Neither Bruce nor the travelling public had taken into account the fertile mind of Thomas Bouch. The young engineer was fascinated by the problem of crossing the Forth and Tay estuaries, and set about designing a ferry to suit the traffic across the two rivers. It has been said that Bouch derived this idea from others also, but at the time no one voiced such a thought, and at this distance in time it is hard to assess his achievements. In any case, Bouch was given the credit for designing the "floating railway" over the Forth. Overcoming the problem of great tidal differences he devised a means of running railway wagons right on to the boat and transporting them across the river, so that if the actual travelling time could not be cut then the port delays might be.

The "floating railway" was the wonder of the age, and here is how Bouch's ramp was described by the correspondent of *The Illustrated London News*.

"Alongside the piers at Burntisland and Granton is an incline or slip, constructed of masonry upon which are laid two lines of rails, the same gauge as the main lines. Upon this incline is placed a heavy moveable platform, 61 feet in length by 21 feet in breadth, framed of timber and resting upon sixteen wheels. To the front of the platform are attached, by means of universal joints, four malleable iron girders, 35 feet long, constructed of boiler-plate, spanning the requisite distance from the platform to the vessel and affording sufficient depth of water for the keel of the vessel to clear the surface of the slip. These girders are raised and lowered by means of a winch on each side of a staging 18 feet high, erected across the platform.

"The whole platform, with the girders, is raised and lowered to suit several heights of tide, by means of a small stationary steam engine, which is also employed in moving trucks off and on board the vessel. The drums and gearing in connection therewith are so arranged as to work the platform, or load and discharge the vessel, with the greatest facility. The vessel can be fully loaded in about five minutes with from thirty to forty wagons, and discharged in about the same time, by two stationary engines ashore."

The boat designed for the service lay long and low on the water, with two huge paddle wheels rising strangely above the deck like the wings of a swan preparing for flight. Separate engines operated the port and starboard paddles to give the vessel more manœuvrability and allow the railway trucks to lie along the deck. Her name was *Leviathan*. This little ship, built by Robert Napier & Sons at Govan, Glasgow, inaugurated the world's first public train ferry, and was the forerunner of the great train ferries of Scandinavia, the English Channel, and elsewhere.

The *Leviathan* was ready by January 1850, and during trials at Burntisland on the last Saturday of the month, the wheeled platform broke away, and swept down the slipway, hurling two workmen into the water. One was rescued, although badly injured, and the other, a man named John Forsyth from Newcastle-on-Tyne, was killed. Forsyth was not the last "man of sober habits and kindly disposition" (as the newspapers described him) to fall victim to one of Bouch's designs.

Despite the misfortune of John Forsyth the directors met at Burntisland on the following Wednesday to make the first full-scale test of the *Leviathan*. They saw twelve trucks of coal and general goods loaded in seven minutes, and then they boarded the ship and crossed to Granton in twenty-five minutes. The wagons were unloaded within three minutes. The entire operation had taken just over half an hour, and the crowds who had gathered at Granton to watch cheered the achievement. The directors were satisfied, too, and adjourned to the Granton Hotel to celebrate.

Oddly, the first voyage was the only one on which the *Leviathan* transported a railway carriage with passengers. The train ferry was used exclusively for goods, and the only people allowed to travel by it were those who missed the regular ferry. There was shelter from neither wind nor rain, and those who were forced to use the floating railway had to seek the lee of the goods wagons, and hope that the journey would be over soon.

The *Leviathan* was a great success, and the Edinburgh, Perth and Dundee company ordered another to operate its Tay ferry. In honour of the builders it named her the *Robert Napier*. The *Robert Napier* later served on the Forth as well, as indeed did many of the other Tay ferry ships, for the vessels were often interchanged between the two estuaries according to circumstances and demand. The company added two other train ferries, the *Carrier* and *Balbirnie*, to its fleet in the next decade.

Passenger services started from a separate pier at Granton, and three vessels named *Granton, Burntisland* and *Forth*, were taken over by the Northern Railway when it bought the ferry. These were soon joined by two Thames-built ships, the *Auld Reekie* and the *Thane of Fife,* and, with the addition of others from time to time, the five operated the ferry until the Forth Bridge was built.

On the whole goods traffic seems to have had the better deal, for passengers were set down at the miserable station which passed for a terminal at Granton, and left to trudge along the cobbled pier to the ship, bearing rugs, wraps, and hand baggage. Perspiring porters "hurled" the heavy luggage along on huge barrows which protested along the cobbles, and whose only brake was the iron shod front supports which screamed agonizingly every time they touched the roadway. The incline of the pier was considerable at low tide, and great Clydesdale horses with clanking chains were used to haul the barrows up from the boats. For the traveller it was deafening and at times frightening.

At the steamer a stern official would demand the traveller's ticket, and force him to set his baggage down on the wet pier and comb his pockets wearily in search of it. And if anyone dared to try to slip his dog past without paying for it, he would be pulled up and asked: "Do you belang to that dug, sir?"

For the passenger who had travelled overnight from England the experience of an early crossing on the ferry was not a pleasant one, and at busy times such as the end of the summer season when the rich migrated south with the swallows, the railway often could not cope with the bulk of luggage and had to leave it behind at Burntisland. The traveller would arrive in Edinburgh with the option of staying the night there until his baggage arrived or of going on without it.

Boswell is reputed to have been unwise enough to remark to Dr. Johnson while crossing the Forth that, after Constantinople and Naples, the prospect was the finest in Europe. To this Dr. Johnson replied dryly: "Water is the same everywhere."

Many travellers in the nineteenth century would have disputed that, for the Granton ferry could be alarming on a stormy day. But if the Forth intimidated the public it did not overawe the seamen, who had a reputation for sharpness of wit and tongue, and who showed no mercy for the cowed passenger.

On a certain stormy day when one of the boats was making a rough passage the pallid, fearful face of a well-known Fife laird so incensed the skipper of the ferry that he leant down from his bridge and bellowed at the terrified young man: "As for you, ye were aye a frightened creature a' your days."

The crossing was not all alarm and discomfort, and to be fair one ought to quote the description of William Ballingall, written in 1872.

"We reached Burntisland just after sun-down, when the tide was back and the town stood clearly defined against the peaceful sky. The shades of evening fell apace as we crossed the ferry, 'tween the gloamin' an' the mirk—an enjoyable sail, for the sea was smooth and there was pleasant music on board, while we feasted our eyes, first on the receding Burntisland lights and afterwards on those we neared along the southern shore from Leith to Granton. Our leading entertainer played the harmonium; he was blind, and if we mistake not is son of the jolly loquacious fiddler whose arguments and songs of the 'Kate Dalrymple' type were wont some years ago to make merry the steamboat passage to Stirling. Our harmonium friend was not overpleased with the singing of his partner, who played the violin, and exhibited his feelings as demonstratively as if he judged his audience to be as blind as himself, for at every discordant tone he shot out his tongue, and contorted his face as if suffering acute pain. His face was most expressive, and, when the music was to his taste, he turned it heavenward, and you would have thought him to be endowed momentarily with the gift of sight, his darkened eye looked upward so intently, with his mouth opened wide as if to drink in the notes."

The Burntisland ferry could be as wild a bit of water as any in the kingdom, and it must have taken many such moonlit nights—and sunny days, too—to eclipse the memories of rough passages.

As Newhaven and then Granton prospered, the Queensferry declined. As early as 1820 traffic was so low that the tacksmen's rents had to be cut; the following year steam was introduced to bolster the ferry, and seven years later Thomas Telford was called in to advise on improving the piers. But it was all to no avail—the decline continued and, indeed, was accelerated by the advent of the railway.

An Act was passed in 1838 for the improvement of the Queensferry, providing for repairs to the piers and defining the limits of the Passage. On the northern shore it stretched from the east side of the East Battery Pier to the west side of Haughend Pier, and on the southern one from the east side of the Long Craig Pier to the west side of Port Edgar Pier, with sufficient space beyond these limits for free and uninterrupted passage of boats.

During the Railway Mania the hopes of the Queensferry trustees were raised by the schemes of the Edinburgh and Perth Railway which was projected by Queensferry, particularly in view of the powerful backing the plan had from other railway companies. But, of course, that fight was won by the Northern and the Queensferry scheme was routed.

Although the defeat of the Queensferry Railway left the Northern master of Fife, its position was by no means secure, and its existence was a continual fight against rising operational costs particularly on the ferries. The company tried running the ferries under contract and on its own, but neither method showed any appreciable saving. Workers had to accept cuts in wages and shareholders reductions in dividends in an effort to keep the railway solvent, and thus it limped along from year to year, incapable of expanding beyond the bounds of its title—the Edinburgh, Perth and Dundee remained essentially a local line, providing services which satisfied no one.

Yet the North British had grown to rule the east coast from Berwick to Edinburgh, and was bursting to extend northwards and westwards, and the Edinburgh and Glasgow had a foot in Fife through the Stirling and Dunfermline Railway. These two companies were watching each other cagily, and it seemed certain that they would come into conflict sooner or later. The battlefield was likely to be the Queensferry, where the trustees of the Passage were in debt and reduced to one ageing steamer which they could not afford to replace.

The contest for the Queensferry was finally triggered when the Edinburgh and Glasgow aligned itself with the Caledonian and Scottish Central, and tried to amalgamate with them in 1860 and 1861, but was refused parliamentary permission to do so. The North British knew then that it was time it consolidated its position.

In the Dunfermine area there was a great deal of dissatisfaction with the Edinburgh, Perth and Dundee. Many Lochgelly mineowners felt that inadequate railway services were hampering their expansion, and the merchants of Dunfermline discovered after the first rapture of a railway connection with the capital that it took about half an hour longer to travel by rail than to go by coach and the Queensferry. Not surprisingly there was ample local support for a line via Queensferry.

In 1860 the scheme was revived and, although the company

was called the Edinburgh and Dunfermline Railway, it was planned to continue all the way to Perth. The company would have running rights over the Edinburgh and Glasgow's main line to a point near Corstorphine, and then branch off on its own to Kirkliston and Queensferry, where it would hold the ferry rights. Starting from North Queensferry again it would run to Dunfermline and on to join the Edinburgh, Perth and Dundee at Sheephousewell.

The engineer of the local Edinburgh and Dunfermline was Thomas Bouch, who had designed the floating railways for the Forth and Tay a decade earlier. Bouch's stay with the Fife company had been short, and he was now building up an extensive and lucrative private practice. The idea was essentially a local one and its projectors wisely sought an established company to run it for them. With this in mind they approached the Edinburgh, Perth and Dundee, which would only accept on condition that the railway should enter Edinburgh by Granton and its Scotland Street tunnel. This was refused, and the North British agreed, not only to operate the railway, but also to put up some of the capital to build it.

When this startling piece of news broke there was a frenzy of opposition. First the Edinburgh and Glasgow and the Scottish Central sought to ensure their monopoly of traffic to the north via Stirling by blocking the southern end of the Queenferry Passage with a line from Ratho, on the main line, to South Queensferry. Next there was a project for a line from Dunfermline to North Queensferry—originally with the backing of the Edinburgh and Glasgow and Scottish Central, but later disowned by them. This railway was projected along the shores of the firth "doing a world of wanton injury to local amenities", the *Railway Times* commented, "and terminating with a huge pier to make which its promoters have omitted to take the requisite powers, and the cost of which, if they had these powers, would amount to more than the whole capital they propose to raise."

The Edinburgh, Perth and Dundee was well aware of its own inadequacy and it began to negotiate secretly with the North British. Thus its 1861 Bill was withdrawn and that, together with the rejection of the opposition schemes, left the way clear for the real fight in the next parliamentary Session. Amalgamation talks with the North British proved too good a secret to keep for long, and all through the early part of 1861 the Press referred to rumours. At the half yearly meeting of the Perth and Dundee company a shareholder raised the question and the chairman admitted that there had been meetings, there would be more, "and ere long a decision would be arrived at one way or the other".

A month later, in September, the two companies called their shareholders together at meetings held simultaneously in Edinburgh, and announced to them that they had decided to unite under the name of the North British. Dividends of the enlarged company were to be divided thus:

When the North British shareholders receive	Edinburgh, Perth and Dundee shareholders will receive
3 per cent	1 per cent
3½ per cent	1¼ per cent
4 per cent	1½ per cent
4½ per cent	1¾ per cent
5 per cent	2 per cent
5½ per cent	2½ per cent
6 per cent	3 per cent

Proprietors on both sides—many of whom held shares in the two companies—were annoyed that the meetings had been arranged in such a way that they did not have a chance to attend both, and among the Edinburgh, Perth and Dundee's shareholders there was also some dissent over the terms the North British had offered. Those from the west of Scotland were particularly frank and said simply that the idea prevailed in their part of the country that the directors must be mad to accept such terms.

The Chairman of the North British summed up the situation when he said that "the Edinburgh, Perth and Dundee shareholders may look down a long lane and see no prospect of a dividend, whereas, under this arrangement, they see a clear dividend in the immediate future."

That was the complete answer: mad or not, the board of the Fife company was determined that the amalgamation should go through, and it faced the shareholders with enough proxy votes in its pocket to ensure a majority of 7,321 for the union.

In the 1862 Session of Parliament the official union of the North British with the Edinburgh, Perth and Dundee and the West of Fife Railway was sought, and the companies jointly promoted their own Queensferry scheme. Once again they were opposed by the block line of the Edinburgh and Glasgow from Ratho to the ferry.

When the Bill for the joint North British–Perth and Dundee scheme reached the Standing Orders committee at Westminster it was discovered that they had only given notice that they wanted permissive powers to take the ferry, but in their Bill they had asked for compulsory powers. Thus the Bill was thrown out, and strong appeals backed by local petitions failed to have it revived in that Session. As the Commons refused to reconsider the Bill the only hope was that the Edinburgh and Glasgow's Bill might also fail, and they could renew the fight on equal terms in 1863.

That is exactly what happened. On 17 July the Bill was thrown out, and the townfolk of Dunfermline and Inverkeithing rang their bells for an hour in jubilation. It seems incredible that people who wanted a railway so badly should rejoice at the failure of any scheme which might bring them one, but they knew that the Edinburgh and Glasgow merely meant to block the North British scheme which would serve them best.

Twelve days after the rout of the Edinburgh and Glasgow, the North British and Edinburgh, Perth and Dundee consolidated their position when the Act for their amalgamation and that of the West of Fife received the Royal Assent. The merger did not produce any magical recovery in dividends, however. At the first general meeting of the united companies a couple of months after the Act was passed an unusually large gathering at the Masonic Hall in Edinburgh was told that the dividend had been cut because of poor trading conditions due to the general recession in the country.

In 1863 the North British brought forward a Bill for a line from Piershill on its main line just east of the Edinburgh terminus to curve round to the old Granton line at Trinity, and continue to Granton and along the shore of the Forth to Queensferry. The ferry was to be bought over, and on the northern shore the railway would be built to Dunfermline. The opposition scheme from Ratho was also renewed, and the result of the parliamentary battle was a victory for the North British, which got its Act for the whole of the line except the stretch from Granton to Queensferry. The Edinburgh and Glasgow was also given permission to build its Ratho–Queensferry railway, but the North British was to be permitted absolute running powers over it. The right to buy the ferry was given to the North British, but if the purchase was not completed within two years the Glasgow company had the right to step in and take it.

The quarrel this might have led to was averted by a decision, born of fear, to amalgamate.

For some years the Edinburgh and Glasgow had operated a "common purse" agreement with the Caledonian and the Scottish Central, and in fact it had endeavoured to amalgamate with them to keep the North British out of the west of Scotland. When the agreement came to an end in the early 1860s the Glasgow company decided to renew it despite strong North British pressure for an east-west union with it instead. The North British was angry at the rejection of its offer, and refused to accept banishment from Glasgow. If the Edinburgh and Glasgow pursued such a policy much longer, it warned, a rival line must inevitably be built between the two cities one day. The Edinburgh and Glasgow would suffer then, and when that happened the Caledonian would not rush to its aid.

At the end of 1863 the "inevitable" happened—plans were announced for a new railway between the two cities under the ominous title Glasgow and North British, and the line was to be maintained and operated by the North British after it was built.

Fear of this, and the other expansionist policies of the North British, compelled the Edinburgh and Glasgow to renounce its allies in the west and amalgamate with the North British. In the words of the *Railway Times* it was a "natural and unimpeachable alliance".

Under the merger the Edinburgh and Glasgow ceased to exist; it was a union which left the North British a power in Scotland, stretching from Tweed and Eden to Tay, and from Forth to Clyde. In Fife its power was absolute.

CHAPTER FIVE

QUESTIONS OF ARITHMETIC

THE first decade of the North British company's existence was a struggle to establish itself; the second was a fight for survival. Then followed the decade of war against the Caledonian.

Union with the Edinburgh and Glasgow came towards the end of the second decade and, although it brought a number of advantages such as the tidying up of the conglomeration of railway stations at Waverley and the running of Sunday trains on the strictly sabbatarian Edinburgh and Glasgow line, it did not establish an era of peace and prosperity.

In fact, war with the Caledonian was intensified because the capture of the Edinburgh and Glasgow meant that the North British was established in the west and had taken a firm step towards the Highlands.

Yet all the advantages were not with the North British; the Caledonian was strongly placed and was manœuvring like fury to block the East Coast company.

The war was waged at all levels—with verbiage in the board-rooms and fisticuffs amongst the station staff. Fares were cut and cut again, and it seemed that one or other must be ruined. So fierce did the quarrel become that an arbitrator had to be appointed to settle their disputes as first one and then the other demanded rights in the other's territory. As always the principal sufferer was the traveller, but who cared, this was war.

The North British realized that its only hope of breaking the Caledonian hold in the north-east would be to eliminate the Forth and Tay ferries, and in this endeavour the East Coast company had one good ally—Thomas Bouch.

Bouch was a man who commanded attention in the North British boardroom, for he had made possible the "floating railway" a decade earlier; yet the proposition he now put forward seemed mad to the directors of the company. Bouch actually proposed to bridge the two estuaries.

As engineer to the Queensferry railway scheme when it was revived in 1860-61, Bouch had thrown out hints that the ferry would one day be replaced by a bridge.

Said the *Railway Times*: "The Forth is not at this ferry more than a mile in breadth, and there is an island in the centre, placed there by Nature to invite construction of a bridge. There are also rock foundations for the piers at intervals which will enable the spans to be of less dimensions than several of our more important railway structures. Of course this notion is not for immediate consultation. It is not likely to be brought before the public until a sufficiency of traffic is secured for this intermediate route".

When the company began to think seriously about its Forth Bridge in 1863 the Queensferry Passage site was rejected because the water was considered too deep, and in any case shipping which sheltered in the bay of St. Margaret's Hope during storms might run against it.

Instead Bouch went four or five miles upstream and chose a site close to Blackness Castle from which the bridge could run to Charlestown on the northern shore. By means of linking lines from a point near Linlithgow the company could be provided with an excellent route north.

At the site chosen the river was over two miles broad, and the greatest depth of water around sixty feet, but this was not the main problem—far more serious was the uncertainty of the river bed. Before the Great Ice Age when Britain was attached to the Continent of Europe, the River Forth eroded a deep valley which subsequently filled with silt to a great depth. As a result when Thomas Wyllie made test borings in the 1860's he found the river bottom extremely uncertain. In May 1864 two bores went down 166 feet at low tide without clearing the silt, and in 1865 another was sunk to 231 feet without reaching rock.

However, Bouch reckoned the bridge was a practical possibility, and that it could be erected for a sum in the region of £500,000. As the bridge would save about £150,000 on the operation of the ferries, repair of piers and maintenance of steamers, the North British directors agreed that it was indeed worth considering. Others were prepared to scoff, especially opposition railways. "The Scottish Central is rather inclined to be witty upon the bridge over the Forth", said the *Railway Times*, "but the shareholders in the N.B. take the matter in right earnest."

One proprietor spoke for many when he said he would rather walk the plank of a bridge than float across the Forth. If it could be built the bridge would be a boon to them all.

The scheme was abandoned in the middle of June 1864, when the Edinburgh and Glasgow amalgamation cropped up and it appeared that the North British might get a road north without the bridge, but in the autumn it was revived and notice was given of an application to Parliament in the ensuing session for powers to build Bouch's bridge.

The bridge was a lattice girder structure two miles and 367 yards long, and carrying on its sixty-one piers a single line of railway more than a hundred feet above the river. In the centre there would be four great spans of 500 feet each, rising to a maximum height of 195 feet above river level. The ironwork would rest on stone piers, which would be sunk 25 feet below the silt bottom, making the total height of the structure 285 feet from the foundation to topmost tip.

The North British was proud of the contribution its bridge would make to the economy of the Kingdom.

"No one acquainted with the resources of Fife, and the impediments to their development, can doubt for a moment the immense stimulus which such a communication with the South of Scotland and with the sister countries would create", stated the report to shareholders in 1865.

The directors' only reservations were on cost and the suitability of the foundations, and already Bouch had reassured

(*Above*) Inchgarvie and North Queensferry from the South Queensferry landing place about the time when the ferrymen were in
dispute with the owners of the Passage over their right to operate
the service. (*Below*) The Queensferry Passage in September, 1802

James Anderson's slender bridge of 1818 was among the earliest
later: "It would hardly have been visible on a dull day, and

Thomas Bouch designed the "floating railway" which came into
first train ferry

planned to span the Queensferry. Of this bridge an engineer said after a heavy gale it would no longer be seen on a clear day either"

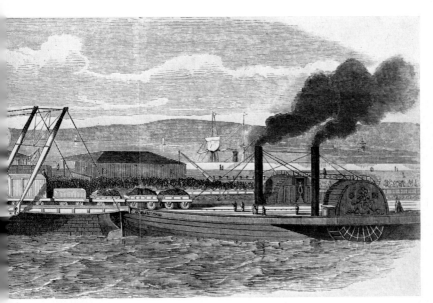

service between Granton and Burntisland in 1850 and was the in the world

Queen Victoria and Prince Albert arrive at Granton Pier in 1842 at the start of their tour of Scotland. The first part of Granton Harbour had been opened on the Queen's coronation day, June 28th, 1838

Sir Thomas Bouch's Forth Bridge was like two giant bridges placed end to end. Building had just been begun when the Tay Bridge, also designed by Bouch, collapsed and the works were soon abandoned

them on the latter. When borings and other tests were completed, the board said, all else will be "a mere question of arithmetic".

The *Railway Times* commented wryly; "Still the 'mere question of arithmetic' will continue to perplex the minds of proprietors, nor may relief from this oppression be obtained until it is finally reported that the structure is completed, and that the estimates are not exceeded".

The North British went ahead with its Bill in the face of opposition from other railways, Alloa Harbour Trust and the Clyde Navigation Trust. These organizations had many searching questions to put to Thomas Bouch on the strength of the bridge and suitability of its foundations, and all were answered confidently by the engineer who had great faith in his plans.

Occasionally Bouch became nettled. When opposing counsel suggested that the pressure of the wind against the foundations might cause the base columns of the bridge to sink he retorted: "Certainly not; I have built bridges of a similar kind and find nothing of the sort."

Counsel wanted to know more about such bridges.

"Was that in a narrow glen, and upon dry land?"

"Yes, it was upon dry land, but it was in Westmorland, which is subject to great gales."

The lawyer persisted. "Supposing it were to happen that one of these columns shown here should get loose in its disc, or that a disc should break, and that it should sink a little lower, what would be the effect upon the structure?"

"You may as well ask me to assume that it will come down."

The lawyer sensed victory. "You do admit that if the pressure of the wind operated so as to make one of these columns sink lower than the others, your bridge must come down?"

"No, I do not even admit that. I had one of the columns of the Bala Bridge gone and there no bridge came down or anything of the sort. I cannot suppose that under any possible circumstances, the thing could happen. . . ."

Victory went to Bouch—and to the North British, which got its Act to build the Great Bridge of Forth. The company was cautious, however, and before committing itself to spending so large a sum of money it decided to erect one of the pillars as a test of the accuracy of the estimates and the suitability of the riverbed for the foundations.

Work on the pier was put in hand within a short time, and in June of 1866 a great crowd gathered at Burntisland to watch an enormous timber raft measuring 60 feet by 80 feet and 7 feet thick, launched and towed out into the firth. On this was to be built a brickwork shell of the pier so that when the masonry was high enough the hollow centre could be filled with 10,000 tons of iron to make it settle securely on the riverbed. The raft was moored in position off Charlestown, and bricklayers began to build the pier, working from the two mooring tugs which had been fitted out as living quarters for them.

At the same time progress was being made on the Tay Bridge project. Towards the end of 1863 there had been a meeting in Dundee at which the scheme was aired, but nothing more happened for another twelve months when Bouch addressed a second gathering of important citizens of the town. This time a committee was set up to promote the scheme and a prospectus was issued for a bridge to be erected by an independent company, but with the support of the North British. A Bill was actually introduced into Parliament, but it was withdrawn because of opposition from other railways, the Dundee Harbour Board, which was jealous for its trade, and the City of Perth, which feared that the project would harm navigation on the river.

In the following Session the plan was renewed by the North British, which resited the bridge and applied to Parliament once more for an Act.

The opposition was equally active, however, and the Caledonian hurried to amalgamate with the Scottish North Eastern Railway to cut off the North British from Aberdeen and the North East. When this Bill looked like going through the directors of the North British found other large "questions of arithmetic" on their minds, and the Tay Bridge Bill was withdrawn once more.

At about the same time the Forth Bridge preparations were halted also. On Friday, 3 August 1866, as the workmen were preparing to sink the raft off Charlestown, they were visited by Richard Hodgson, Chairman of the company, and a few other directors, who informed them that work was to stop at once and the raft was to be towed back to Burntisland and dumped. All of the workmen were then sacked. The experiment had cost the North British £34,390, and had proved nothing, but the company knew that if it had allowed the pier to be put in place and then called off the project, it would be even more costly to demolish the unwanted pillar.

The abandonment of the two bridges was a sign of troubles to come. When the half-yearly report was issued and shareholders found that their dividends were being paid by warrants which could be cashed only at some future date when the company had enough in the bank to honour them, taunts of deceit and conspiracy were thrown at Hodgson and his board.

The Glasgow shareholders met and decided to press for a committee of inquiry to be set up, and when the shareholders' meeting was called the room was filled to bursting point with two camps which hissed and cheered Hodgson's entrance like the arrival of a prizefighter in the ring. The hissers were in the majority, and Hodgson knew that he would have to yield. despite a claim that he had in his hand proxies representing £2,700,000 worth of stock, not to mention a further £300,000 worth which had arrived too late for him to make use of it.

James White of Overstoun, who led the Glasgow faction, pressed for the committee of inquiry and he had his way. The committee issued its report at the beginning of November, and this painted a damning picture.

The accountancy indulged in by the company "was not merely one of general deception of the shareholders and misrepresentation of the company's affairs; it was not merely deliberate falsification of the accounts from year to year, so as to show to the shareholders and divide among them a revenue which was not in existence and was known not to have been earned, but it was a careful and most ingenious fabrication of imaginary account, begun and carried on from time to

75

time for the purpose of supporting the falsified half-yearly statements of revenue and the general mis-representation of affairs."

Although the directors knew that the company was living beyond its income, bolstered by bank loans, they had spent £260,000 on parliamentary expenses in four years—and £79,000 of that was still owing.

The report ended with a section on "remedial measures", the first of which was the replacement of the board of directors.

The shareholders were called together at the Music Hall in Edinburgh on Wednesday, 15 November, and in preparation both factions got to work rallying support. Meetings were held in many parts of the country, and at these resolutions were passed and spokesmen elected. In Glasgow, London, Manchester and Leeds the resignation of Hodgson was demanded, but in Hull and Cheltenham he was asked to stay, and Liverpool, prettily facing both ways, deplored the conduct of all—Hodgson for his chicanery and the committee of inquiry for exposing him and so damaging the company.

The Music Hall was packed on the 15th—it would have been odd had it been otherwise, for free passes had been issued for all holders of stock worth £50 or more to travel from Newcastle, Carlisle, Perth, Glasgow, Dundee and Berwick. Hodgson was absent, but sent a letter to say that he had suffered from "a painful attack in the head" for several days, and had been forced to abandon the journey at Retford.

Hodgson's presence would not have made a scrap of difference, for the investigating committee turned up at the Music Hall with proxies worth £5,000,000 of stock in answer to the £1,500,000 held by Hodgson's friends. Nevertheless the meeting lasted five hours, two of which were taken up by a harangue from the chairman of the committee of investigation.

Hodgson and his supporters were duly voted out of office and a new board was chosen to set the North British on its feet again. In command was John Stirling of Kippendavie, a Scottish laird who had already proved master of the Caledonian, and who seemed the only man shrewd enough both to revive the company and vanquish its enemies.

Stirling was born in 1811, and in 1816, within the space of a year, he succeeded to the estates of Kippendross and Kippendavie in Perthshire on the deaths of his father and grandfather. Stirling could have lived out his life as a country gentleman, and indeed he made his mark by the excellent husbandry of his estates; but he chose a career in business.

His first interest in railways came through his local line, the Dunblane, Doune and Callander Railway, which opened in 1858, and when the Scottish North Eastern was in trouble he was called in, and built it up again so speedily that he was able to exact excellent terms when it amalgamated with the Caledonian in 1866.

As the man who had held the Caledonian he was the natural choice to lead the North British through its most difficult years. The Laird of Kippendavie remained in charge of the company until his death in 1882.

Unfortunately Stirling's policy renewed the war with the Caledonian so that it reached a new intensity, and Scotland despaired of sanity ever returning to her railway boardrooms.

Because of the Caledonian war many proprietors refused to back Stirling, and one must admit some justice on their side when they laid figures before Stirling in the early 1870's to show that the cost of all the Scottish railway schemes then in Parliament—many of them competing in whole or in part—would be £8,376,650.

Stirling refused to be thwarted by these people, many of whom he accused of being concerned merely because they had money in both companies, and were afraid they were going to lose it.

Stirling's family motto was "Gang forward", and that spirit was carried into the North British boardroom. His years of rule were the most momentous in the whole life of the company.

Although the Forth and Tay bridges were still recognized as essential to the North British it was obvious that the railway would have to live without either for a number of years. In 1867, therefore, the company bought the Queensferry at last under powers granted by the Act of 1863. The price was £4,700 and included the ageing steamer *William Adam*, which continued to operate the service until the mid-1870's when it was replaced by a new screw steamship built at Kinghorn.

The directors of the North British were proud enough of their achievements to give their own names to the ferries and this latest ship was called the *John Beaumont*, after the Vice-Chairman.

The *John Beaumont* was the first screw vessel on the ferry and she was unpopular after the old paddle steamer William Adam. Her lack of manœuvrability was proved early on a winter's evening shortly before Christmas, 1878, when she was driven against the pier at North Queensferry and sank. There were no passengers on board and the crew all got ashore safely, but the incident was seized upon by her critics who gave the North British board advice in verse:

> Directors o' the N.B.R.
> You ne'er should try to lift her;
> There's mony better boats by far—
> The *Willie* e'en was swifter.

> You'll find that paddles beat the screw,
> Although ye've sair misca'ed em;
> And nane can wish a smarter crew
> Then sailed the *Willie Adam*.

Ignoring the first piece of advice the North British did lift the vessel, but they fitted her with paddles and thereafter she sailed the Queensferry for many years.

Improvements were made to the Granton ferry and rail route, too. The branch from the main line at Piershill to join the Leith and Granton line at Trinity was built, and the North British's Granton traffic began to use this instead of the Scotland Street tunnel on 2 March 1868.

The tunnel was then closed, but it is still there, unseen and unknown to many citizens of Edinburgh who use Waverley station regularly. After its closure the tunnel was used for wagon storage until 1887 when the Glasgow firm of Robert and John Paton had the bright idea of leasing the tunnel for the cultivation of mushrooms. Thus the Scottish Mushroom

Company was founded, and for sixteen years mushroom beds flourished beneath Princes Street. In 1903 a parastic fungus attacked the mushrooms and the company had to abandon its mushroom beds. Five years later a fresh attempt was made to revive the industry, but again fungus blighted the crops, and in 1917 the Scottish Mushroom Company had to go into liquidation. A last attempt to re-establish the Scotland Street Tunnel mushroom beds was made in 1927, but once more it failed when the fungus attacked the crops.

In 1938 the London and North Eastern Railway fitted the tunnel out as a wartime control centre and staff air raid shelter. A number of buildings were erected, including an emergency control room and a first-aid room, and the tunnel was finally fitted out to accommodate 3,000 people. During the war Scottish Command and the Ministry of Aircraft Production considered using the tunnel, but both plans were dropped, and the tunnel remained empty.

The last person to use the Scotland Street Tunnel was a certain Mr. Jha, an Indian atomic scientist then studying at Edinburgh University, who found it suitably remote from atmospheric radiation of the city above for his experiments into the measurement of radio activity. Mr. Jha's brief tenancy completes the story of the Scotland Street Tunnel, for it lies empty and abandoned today.

In the hectic years when the Granton ferry was a busy crossing a number of boats were added to the train ferry and passenger fleets. The first of the new "floating railways" was the *Balbirnie*, constructed in 1861, and then the *Kinloch* was added after the North British took over. In 1867 a vessel called the *Nymph* was bought for the run and the last of the train ferries was the *Midlothian* which was built in 1881.

During this time three passenger ships were added also— the *John Stirling*, the *James Cox*, and the *William Muir*, which was perhaps the best known of all the Granton ferries.

With these vessels the ferry served the traveller more or less satisfactorily—if uncomfortably in wind and rain, tempest and sleet. On all but the finest days of summer it remained an ordeal to descend from the warmth of the carriage, struggle along the quay, and jostle to board the ship. And as the ferry butted its way over the angry water many eyes turned towards the narrows of Inchgarvie and lips formed a prayer that a bridge might soon be built to save the traveller from the merciless firth.

CHAPTER SIX

MR. BOUCH'S CROWNING TRIUMPH

IMPOVERISHED as the North British then was, John Stirling knew from the outset of his reign that to break the Caledonian's hold and keep his company alive the Forth and Tay must be bridged. He therefore took the first opportunity to revive the Tay Bridge plans, and present them to the public again.

Stirling travelled to Dundee to meet the Town Council and the Harbour Trustees on 7 September 1869. He was enthusiastic and reassured his audience on the score of finance—the bridge would save his company £9,000 a year which it paid on tolls for the use of the line between Broughty Ferry and Dundee, and that—together with the economy of discontinuing the ferry— would go a long way towards paying interest on the large sum needed for the project. He therefore intended to recommend his shareholders to guarantee 5¼ per cent on the stock.

On the engineering aspect of the scheme Thomas Bouch held the audience under his spell as he described the squat ribbon of stone and iron which would reach out from Wormit Bay in Fife to the Angus shore at Magdalen Point. The riverbed was mostly rock, so the bridge should present no insuperable engineering difficulties. In fact to Thomas Bouch it was all very straightforward.

Both councillors and trustees heard the speakers with pleasure, and heartily approved the scheme.

Stirling was a fair enough man not to try and bully his proprietors into sanctioning the bridge, nor yet to use proxies to overcome opposition. But he was determined to have his way when the shareholders met on 12 November, and long before the meeting took place he had issued a statement on the cost of the bridge, which showed the advantages it would bring to the North British. Some thought, rightly, that the revival of the scheme would be tantamount to a declaration of war against the Caledonian, and others opposed it on the grounds that it could not be built within the estimates. However, the opinion of many proprietors on cost was voiced by one who said of the £350,000 figure which had been quoted for bridge and connecting lines; "Build it for that and I am content—the sooner you do the better". And to show how doubtful he was of the possibility he proceeded to vote against the scheme.

By the day of the November meeting Stirling did not have to worry about that vote; he had in his pocket a tender from the firm of Butler and Pitts, offering to build the bridge in the space of three years and well within the estimates. Armed with this he won leave to apply to Parliament for an Act to build the Tay Bridge.

As a double check the plans and estimates were laid before a neutral engineer, Thomas E. Harrison, who reported back:

"I have examined all details of the design for the railway bridge over the Tay above Dundee, and I have had all the different parts carefully calculated, and I have much pleasure in stating that great care has been taken in the design, and that it is sufficiently strong in all its parts".

The opposition was now crumbling—Perth's disapproval was only a gesture, for Bouch had modified his plan to give greater clearance for shipping in mid-channel. This was done by raising the height of the girders in the central portion so that the railway, which ran at the level of the top of the girders for most of the way across, would pass at the level of the bottom of the girders. These spans became known as the high girders, and much was to be heard of them later.

The civic authorities of Dundee were behind the project, even if their pride was injured when they saw the text of the Bill and found that it contained clauses permitting them to subscribe to the capital. To incorporate such clauses without so much as a by-your-leave was an outrage, and they told the

North British so forthrightly and speedily. Stirling did not argue; the clauses were dropped at once.

That left the Bill with only one opponent—the Caledonian Railway. In Parliament the Caledonian argued that the North British could not afford to build the bridge, but this made a poor plea, especially when everyone knew that the real reason was a venomous mixture of hatred, jealousy and fear. The Caledonian's arguments were soon disposed of and the Bill went through Parliament quite easily. The Act received the Royal Assent on 15 July 1870.

Thomas Bouch and the builders were busy men throughout the autumn and the following spring, although their work was frequently hampered by the sort of wild and stormy weather that the Tay estuary sometimes knows. Then came a more severe setback when Mr. Pitts, of the contracting firm, died and his company did not feel able to carry on with the contract. All was well, though. The bridge was put out for tender again, and the North British was greatly pleased when the well-known and experienced firm of Charles de Bergue & Company actually tendered £12,000 lower than the original estimate of Butler and Pitts. The offer was speedily accepted.

When a jetty had been built for landing materials and foundations had been excavated for the first three pillars on the Fife shore a small ceremony was held for the laying of the first stone. There were few onlookers with neither bands nor demonstration, and when a toast had been drunk to the success of the bridge work was resumed quickly.

Through the remaining months of 1871 and the first quarter of 1872 the tall narrow pillars of Bouch's bridge began to stride out into the estuary. The work was not easy for the contractors who were hampered by bad weather, strikes, and then the uncertainty of the river bed. Although test borings had shown a good rock bottom for most of the way across, the builders found in practice that this was not so and the bottom was sand and gravel which could not bear the tall, narrow piers which Bouch had designed. The engineer was asked to reconsider his plans, and this he readily did, placing the pillars on the broader base more suited to the great weight which the bridge would carry. Other alterations which Bouch made were the substitution of iron for brick in the upper part of the piers to reduce weight, and the replanning of the high girders. Originally Bouch had designed fourteen equal spans in the centre of the bridge, but this he altered to eleven of 245 feet and two of 227 feet. There were thus thirteen high girders.

In the middle of all this the Tay Bridge Company again lost its contractor. Charles de Bergue died in the spring of 1874, and the contract was relinquished by his company. Once again a new builder was sought and after several months Messrs. Hopkins, Gilkes & Company of London and Middlesbrough, tendered and were accepted.

Although a foundry was set up at Wormit to cast the girders and save the delay of transporting them from the North of England, it was now obvious that considerably longer would be needed to build the bridge, and an extension of time was sought. Intense, lingering frost halted the works at the start of 1875, and then the river bottom gave more trouble. It was hard to know which was the greater enemy.

Little could be done about the weather, but the ingenuity with which the construction problems were being overcome was a lesson to every engineer of the day. Pause at Perth, the editor of *Engineering* advised those successful railway men who were returning from "the sportsman's carnival" of the Highland shooting season in 1875—pause at Perth, and travel down the Tay to inspect the bridge. Engineers considered the bridge "one of the most interesting and instructive engineering works anywhere in progress".

The magazine admitted that the structure was not going to enhance the estuary in any aesthetic sense. "Even when finished the viaduct can hardly constitute a pleasing feature in the scenery," it admitted. "Two miles of an ugly type of lattice girders can hardly be ignored, and will blend but poorly with the magnificent mountain background and thickly wooded slopes."

Indeed, Bouch had demonstrated that he was a hard-headed practical man little troubled with artistic squeamishness. And that was just the type of man to build a greater Britain.

Early in 1876 the directors of the bridge company followed the advice of *Engineering* and held their board meeting at Dundee in order that they might inspect the works. They declared themselves greatly pleased, and Bouch was no doubt highly gratified.

In the early days of May the first of the high girders was added, and the end of the great task seemed in sight at last. Although two of the girders were blown off in a storm in February of the following year work proceeded smoothly and it was announced in June 1877, that the contractors had arranged for a trial run over the bridge on 15 September. That estimate was near enough. On the last day of August the directors gathered to watch the last two girders hoisted to their full height, and on Saturday, 22 September, the last rail was laid and an engine ran the length of the bridge. For the remainder of the day and the whole of the Sunday thousands of citizens of Dundee were allowed to walk over the bridge and satisfy their curiosity. Then the directors made their own ceremonial inspection and crossing.

The bridge was now complete, but it could not be used because the connecting lines were not all ready, and would not be for a considerable time. That was not altogether a bad thing for it would give the company more time to test the bridge and the public an opportunity to become used to the idea of it before they were asked to travel on it.

In the dying days of 1877 ballast trains were run across the bridge regularly, and contractors and railway company representatives met and approved the accounts at a single sitting. The workmen were now paid off and the bridge was handed over by the builders.

Mr. Albert Grothe, the superintending engineer, hurried off to Glasgow to repeat his popular lecture on the building of the bridge, the Government inspector was invited to make his formal examination of it, the public walked down to the Tay to admire it, and William McGonagall honoured it with his newfound gift of poetry.

Beautiful Railway Bridge of the Silvery Tay!
With your numerous arches and pillars in so grand array,

85

And your central girders, which seem to the eye
To be almost towering to the sky.
The greatest wonder of the day,
And a great beautification to the River Tay,
Most beautiful to be seen,
Near by Dundee and the Magdalen Green.

McGonagall eulogized the bridge, its builders, and its beauty,
and he asked for protection for those who travelled on it:

Beautiful Railway Bridge of the Silvery Tay!
I hope that God will protect all passengers by night and by day,
And that no accident will befall them while crossing
The Bridge of the Silvery Tay,
For that would be most awful to be seen,
Near by Dundee and the Magdalen Green.

Major-General Charles Scrope Hutchinson, the Government
inspector, arrived on the morning of Monday, 25 February to
begin his "very responsible duties", and was met by ex-Provost
Cox, Chairman of the Tay Bridge Company, and Thomas
Bouch. The major-general began work on the high girders,
and asked for six great locomotives to be run across the spans
at speed and then to be stopped on the bridge. The load was
about 360 tons compared with the 162 tons which a goods
train would weigh in daily service. A passenger train would
weigh even less. By afternoon all of the large spans had been
tested, and Hutchinson began work on the smaller ones. His
inspection was completed on the Tuesday, and he spent the
Wednesday examining the piers, and sailing across the estuary
to look for damage resulting from his tests.

Bouch watched every move with the interest of a father
whose child was being paraded before the judges at a baby
show. Pompously he reminded the curious that the object
of the tests should be borne in mind—they were to ascertain
beyond every possible doubt that the work, in design, material
and execution was equal to its requirements, making the security of the public as far as these three essentials were concerned,
an absolute certainty.

Hutchinson went off to prepare his report, and Bouch waited

—confidently no doubt, for he had great faith in his bridge. The report soon came and, apart from a few minor alterations and renewals of material here and there, Hutchinson declared that he saw no reason why the Board of Trade should object to the bridge being used for passenger traffic. However, it would "not be desirable that trains should run over the bridge at a high rate of speed" he added, and suggested "twenty-five miles an hour as a limit which should not be exceeded". Hutchinson had one other qualification: "I should wish if possible to have an opportunity of observing the effects of a high wind when a train of carriages is running over the bridge". That was the most important sentence Charles Scrope Hutchinson ever wrote, for it saved his reputation, his career, and perhaps even his life.

The bridge was now ready, but it was another two months before its connecting lines were completed and the trains could run through from Burntisland to Dundee. Royalty declined to attend the opening, but the Tay Bridge directors made the most of the occasion. "In order to give as much eclat as possible to the opening ceremonies" dignitaries from the leading railways throughout Britain were invited, together with Members of Parliament, Scottish nobles, provosts, senior magistrates, and town clerks from almost every burgh in the country.

Just before ten o'clock a special train left Edinburgh for Granton where the paddle steamer *John Stirling* waited to take the guests to Burntisland to join another train for Leuchars. On the progress through Fife more passengers were picked up at each station, and then at Leuchars another train arrived from Tayport with the Dundee guests. The trains were joined up to make a total of 1,500 people for the journey across the bridge to Dundee. Thousands of Dundee folk joined in the celebrations by cheering the train from vantage points at Magdalen Green and the Esplanade. After a ceremony at the new Tay Bridge Railway Station, 600 gentlemen adjourned to the Albert Institute to dine and see the freedom of the grateful burgh conferred on John Stirling and Thomas Bouch.

Those who had cheered from the Fife shore and the esplanade below the bridge were left to find out the benefits of the new railway for themselves, and in this they had the poetic assistance of William McGonagall:

> ... the thrifty housewives of Newport.
> To Dundee will often resort,
> Which will be to them profit and sport,
> By bringing cheap tea, bread, and jam,
> And also some of Lipton's ham.

The bridge was just a year old when both it and its designer received the accolade. The Queen, who had declined to attend the opening celebrations, decided to travel by way of Dundee and the bridge on her return from Balmoral in June 1879. It was not much of a royal visit so far as Dundee was concerned, and the city had to be content with a brief pause at the station while addresses of welcome and bouquets were presented. The ceremonial completed, the royal train steamed out of the station and on to the bridge.

It was a splendid summer's evening, with the sun reflecting the still waters of the river and a slight haze lying over the Fife shore. The train rumbled gently over the first spans and then disappeared into the high girders. As it emerged again the band of the training ship *Mars* struck up the National Anthem, and the boys drawn up on the deck presented arms and fired a salute. Her Majesty was impressed with her martial subjects; she was impressed with the magnificence of the bridge; and undoubtedly she was impressed with the engineering achievements of Thomas Bouch, who was summoned to Windsor Castle before the month was out to receive the accolade.

The royal journey and Bouch's knighthood set the seal of success upon the Tay Bridge and the North British Railway as well. It brought a great surge of traffic not only to Dundee, but to the whole of the north-east. Goods traffic also was increasing encouragingly, and the industrialists of Fife knew that it would only be a matter of time until the Forth was bridged and their country was opened up properly. The Forth Bridge had already been a long time building, and was still far from completion.

Early in 1871 the *Dundee Advertiser* had brought to light James Anderson's 1818 plans for the "bridge of chains" across the Forth, and these were shown to the directors of the North British. It has been said that Thomas Bouch had few original ideas, but was skilful at adapting and copying those of others, yet one can only guess whether the new bridge which he planned for the Forth was based on Anderson's delicate metal ribbon. The fact remains that he abandoned the idea of a girder bridge at Blackness and substituted a suspension one at Queensferry.

Bouch's design looked like two great suspension bridges set end to end, with the division between the two parts at Inchgarvie Island. Great pairs of towers supported the "bridges", the pillars of the southern section being located on Inchgarvie and on the shelf where the river deepens off South Queensferry, and those of the northern one on the island and on the Fife shore. The pillars to carry the bridge would be close on 600 feet tall, and each of the two spans 1,600 feet long. For the layman comparisons were made with Scottish landmarks to bring home to them the immensity of the structure. The pillars would soar as high as the top of Arthur's Seat above Princes Street, and the spans would extend as far along Princes Street as from Frederick Street to Waverley Bridge.

This great bridge of Forth was to carry a single line of railway 150 feet above high water level.

The Tay Bridge had just been begun, and was considered the most stupendous ever erected, but this would eclipse it.

The North British line already ran to Queensferry—it had been built from Ratho Junction to Dalmeny in 1866 and to Queensferry in 1868. Now an Act was applied for to join this to the company's Fife lines by way of Bouch's Bridge. The capital was to be £1,250,000, and while the Bill was being put forward the scheme was laid before four of the greatest experts of the day, William H. Barlow, Sir John Hawkshaw, George P. Bidder, and Thomas Harrison.

The North British, while anxious to see the Forth bridged, was by now fully occupied with the Tay project where the riverbed was already giving trouble, and it did not want to start work at Queensferry just as that moment. In fact it did not want to tackle the project, without some outside support, preferably from the great English companies which were anxious to obtain an East Coast route to the north.

Stirling told his shareholders at their meeting in Edinburgh in March 1873; "I am not prepared to pledge myself to it till we see the nature of the reports (of the engineers), and what the southern companies will do. If these reports are not decidedly favourable, and the southern companies do not come forward and support it, the North British will hear nothing more of the Forth Bridge."

The engineers reported favourably on Bouch's design, although they were troubled by the effect the pressure of the wind might have upon so great a surface in the exposed Forth Valley. They consulted the Astronomer Royal who replied that the greatest force to which the bridge was likely to be subjected was ten pounds a square foot.

The engineers concurred, and on the strength of this Bouch did not consider it necessary to make any special wind pressure allowance on his low, long Tay Bridge.

The Forth Bridge was authorized on 5 August 1873. The company now had an Act, a plan by the engineering giant of the moment, and a favourable report from experts. Within a short time it also had reports which promised a firm rock base where the pillars of the bridge were to be placed.

"It is confidently anticipated that the erection of the bridge will be commenced at no distant date," reported *Engineering*, but months turned into years and nothing was done, for the North British was far too busy bridging the Tay.

However, to secure its hold on Fife it took over the Dunfermline and Queensferry Railway which had been authorized in the early 1860's, and built the line. With that line open in 1877 the North British was ready to make maximum use of the Forth Bridge as soon as it was built.

The successful completion of the Tay Bridge in September 1877, gave impetus to the Forth Bridge scheme, and within a month meetings had been held in Edinburgh and London and an agreement concluded between the North British, the North Eastern, the Great Northern and the Midland for the building of the bridge. Each of the four railways would guarantee enough traffic over it to equal 6 per cent dividend on the capital required. A Bill giving the necessary powers to the "Big Four" was immediately introduced.

The design to be used was that of Thomas Bouch, or as *Engineering* put it (to the great man's annoyance no doubt) "Mr. Banch, C.E. who has made such a name for himself in connection with the Tay Bridge".

Although the agreement among the four railway companies assured the possibility of building the bridge, it took time to get so huge a project under way, and time was the one commodity of which the company had little. To conform to the letter of the Act work had to begin by 1 October 1878, but the companies were not at all keen to do this as they were trying to persuade the Board of Trade to allow them to lower the height of their bridge by 20 feet, and cut both the length and cost. Clearance of 150 feet had been allowed to let naval vessels pass upstream to shelter in the Bay of St. Margaret's Hope, but, with sail giving way to steam, ships were no longer so tall and the bridge company considered the extra height unnecessary.

Naturally there were objections to this, particularly from the ports further up the Forth, and the Board of Trade convened an inquiry in Edinburgh at the beginning of September. This resulted in a rebuff for the bridge promoters who had to adhere to the agreed height, and start the work by 1 October as laid down in the Act.

The Board of Trade's decision came towards the end of September, and the arranging of the ceremonial laying of the foundation stone, without which so splendid a project could not possibly start, had to be rushed—it did not seem to have occurred to the directors that the same foundation stone would suit regardless of height of the bridge, and that they could carry on with the ceremony without waiting for the Board of Trade's decision. In any case, the contractor was left to arrange the ceremony with neither the aid nor the presence of the directors of the bridge company or the sponsoring railways.

On the morning of the last day of September a special train left Edinburgh with a few guests, and only one director of the North British, who was at great pains to explain that he was there in a private capacity. The Press were furious that they had not been invited, and made their own way to Queensferry and hired their own boats to follow the official party to Inchgarvie.

The ceremony on the island had to be brief since the foundation stone was to be laid below high water level and—as the contractor pointed out—"time and tide no man bide". A minister offered up a prayer, Mrs. Thomas Bouch laid the stone, and the reporters who had now effected a landing, joined in the three cheers for the success of the bridge. After that all returned to Queensferry where luncheon awaited the official party at the Hawes Inn, and speeches were made eulogizing the bridge, its designer, and its sponsors.

The general manager of the North British Railway, who had now joined the party, referred to the magical increase in traffic which the Tay Bridge had brought. Now they were looking forward to the completion of the Forth Bridge which would further improve trade to the north. He reminded the guests of the debt they owed to Bouch who had for a long time "been improving and perfecting" his scheme for crossing the Forth. "I venture to say," he told them, "that this gigantic undertaking, when completed, will be the crowning triumph in Mr. Bouch's distinguished professional career."

Within days the work was suspended when the pier reached high water mark. They had complied with the terms of the Act, but a lot had to be done yet before the company was ready to begin any serious work on the bridge.

In fact it was 4 April the following year that Mr. John Waddell, of Edinburgh, resumed work on the brick pier where the ceremony had taken place seven months before.

"It is intended that the construction of this great engineering work shall now be actively proceeded with," declared *Engineering*, and this time work really did begin. A month later it was reported: "Already a massive column of brickwork is beginning to show itself on the western end of Inchgarvie".

Large quantities of material now lay at North Queensferry station ready for shipment to the island, and a start was made at Burntisland on the connecting railways.

By the time the Queen made her crossing the Tay Bridge was becoming a regular feature of the scenery—almost a back number. "The Tay Bridge is looked upon as a grand affair," said the Press, "but it sinks into insignificance when compared with the Forth Bridge."

In mid August the directors of the bridge company examined the tenders for the ironwork of the bridge, but they could not make up their minds, and discussed the matter several times again in the following weeks.

In the meantime borings were begun for another bridge over the Forth—at Alloa. Here a steam ferry had plied for a number of years from the South Alloa terminus of the Larbert branch of the Caledonian Railway to Alloa on the northern shore of the Forth. The new bridge was designed to carry a single line of railway across the river, by seventeen spans, two of 100 feet, two of 80 feet, and thirteen of 68 feet. The piers rose 24 feet above the high water mark, and some of them were as much as 70 feet below the bed of the river. The Alloa Bridge was paid for by the Caledonian and opened in 1885. The North British had running powers over it in return for granting the Caledonian the use of their station at Alloa.

However, the Queensferry bridge occupied more minds than did this minor affair at Alloa. In December negotiations were concluded for the issue of capital, and with the railway companies guaranteeing traffic it was assured of success. The City article in *The Times* encouraged the scheme, and letters to the editor pointing out the unprecedented risks involved, asking what security the contractor had been asked to give, or what the shareholders' position would be if the bridge was not completed, were never published. These letters were referred to in the City column and refuted by a statement that Parliament had approved the design, and ensured that all was in order. Furthermore, the experience gained on the Tay Bridge would afford ample basis for safe estimates on cost. The official notices inviting subscription made no reference to the fact that there was anything unusual in the scheme, and it is not surprising that the whole capital was forthcoming within a few days.

The Forth Bridge Railway Company directors, and new shareholders, had a very happy Christmas, and sat back to await 1880. The new year would see the project under way—properly under way this time.

On 27 December the *Railway Times* reprinted an article from *The Times* in praise of the bridge, and its designer "Sir Thomas Bouch, C.E., whose greatest achievement hitherto—the Tay Bridge—has turned out a splendid success—a success recognized and endorsed in the honour of knighthood awarded to him since its completion."

A day later, on the last Sunday of the year, one of the worst storms Scotland had known in years blew across Edinburgh as the afternoon train from Waverley made the short journey to Granton where the *John Stirling* awaited. It promised to be a bitter, uncomfortable crossing, with wind churning the firth into foaming waves which broke over the harbour wall and threatened to drench the travellers. In the darkening afternoon the passengers must have looked upstream for the comfort of a glimpse of Bouch's bridge which would end the agony of the crossing. Burntisland was gained and the train set off through Fife, picking up and setting down passengers on the way. At Leuchars the tickets were collected and the little train comprising a third class coach, a first class one, two more thirds, a second class one, and guard's van pulled out. The ticket collector reckoned up his tickets. There were fifty-seven passengers for Dundee, five or six for Broughty Ferry, and a couple of season ticket holders. Manning the train were driver, fireman and guard, and two other guards going off duty had also boarded the train. Seventy souls were bound for Dundee.

The driver slowed at the south end of the bridge to take up the baton without which no train was allowed to cross. Signalman Thomas Barclay advised the cabin on the northern end of the bridge that the train was on its way. He entered the time in his book. It was 7.13.

John Watt, a surfaceman who had gone to Barclay's cabin to keep him company, watched from the window while the signalman entered the time in the book and made up the stove fire. A strong gale was blowing from west-south-west, almost directly across the bridge and, although the moon was full, cloud made the night quite dark.

Watt kept looking at the train. Sparks began to appear from the wheels after it had gone 200 yards. Suddenly there was a bright flash of light, and in an instant total darkness—the tail lamp of the train, the sparks, the flash all disappearing at the same moment.

Slowly came the awful realization—the bridge was down.

CHAPTER SEVEN

NEW PLANS

T H E contract for the construction of the Forth bridge went to a Scottish engineer—to the only firm north of the Border to tender, in fact. The company was neither long-established nor famous, having been founded only ten years earlier by a young blacksmith with £84 capital. The man who dared to tender when greater engineers hesitated was forty-year-old William Arrol.

The origins of the Arrol family lay just beyond the Highland line on Loch Lomondside, but William's great-grandfather crossed the Clyde to settle in Renfrewshire at the time of the Forty-Five Rebellion. When William was born in February 1839, his father was employed as a cotton spinner at the village of Houston, near Paisley, and the boy received his early education at Johnstone close by, first at a dame's school and then in William Taylor's penny-a-week school where the master stirred his porridge as he drilled his pupils. Schooldays were brief for William Arrol, and before he reached the age of ten he was earning half-a-crown a week as a thread boy at a Johnstone cotton mill.

In 1850 the family moved to Paisley, and there William entered the turning shop of Coats's thread mill. Three years later he was apprenticed to a blacksmith in Paisley, and with extra pence earned singeing sheep's heads for local housewives he bought himself fine clothes and paid for night school lessons and books.

When his apprenticeship was completed work was not always

easy to find, and Arrol had long walks in search of jobs in between spells of employment at Clydeside shipyards. However, he was hardly out of his teens when he landed a plum job as foreman at Laidlaw's Engineering Works in the East End of Glasgow. With Laidlaw's he built the iron pier at Deal in 1865, and in the same year made his first bridge—to carry a railway over the streets of Greenock. The following year he built the West Pier at Brighton, and in 1868 he set up on his own. Again life was hard for Arrol as he established his company. The first important task his firm undertook was spanning the Clyde at Bothwell for the North British Railway in 1875, and in the same year he was given the commission for the first of his two great Caledonian bridges over the Clyde at Broomielaw in Glasgow.

When the Forth Bridge scheme was mooted William Arrol had the courage to tender for its construction, and his bid was accepted. Throughout the autumn of 1879 he was busy preparing to begin construction, but then came that stunning blow on the last Sunday of the year when the Tay Bridge fell.

Arrol ignored the gossip and rumour which followed, and worked steadily on. It must have been hard to pretend that the disaster had not undermined confidence in the great Forth Bridge, yet the only sign of doubt apparent was an announcement in an Edinburgh newspaper that application would again be made to the Board of Trade for permission to lower the height of the bridge by 10 or 15 feet.

On 15 January notices were ordered to be served on the Earl of Rosebery to take some of his ground near South Queensferry which was required for the bridge, and the following week Arrol visited Queensferry to prepare equipment for the building of workshops and installation of plant.

Slowly Scotland was beginning to recover from the numbing horror of the Tay Bridge catastrophe. Shock gave way to anger, and naturally that anger was directed against Thomas Bouch. Bouch had designed the bridge which had taken so many lives; Bouch had also designed the Forth Bridge which was admitted to be on a far, far greater scale than the one which had just fallen. Although the court of inquiry was only beginning to assemble its evidence and a verdict on the cause of the disaster was still months away, everybody blamed Bouch's design. His past achievements were forgotten, and the public would not trust him now to throw a plank across a burn, let alone span the majestic Queensferry.

The Forth Bridge Company announced that a commission would re-examine the design and chose the same group of engineers as had reported favourably on the project in 1873, with the exception of Bidder who had died. *Engineering* expressed the astonishment and fury of many when it stated that Barlow, Hawkshaw and Harrison had already committed themselves on the design in 1873, and an inquiry by them now would be worse than useless. A new and independent committee was needed, not so much to reconsider already approved designs as to decide whether in fact a huge suspension bridge was suitable for such heavy and continuous traffic at all.

Engineering was not sure that the shareholders had not been duped. "It has never been clearly stated in terms which a country parson and the usual run of shareholders could understand, whether the railways guarantee absolutely the interest on the share capital whatever may happen, or whether it is only a guarantee after the bridge has been opened, and while it is maintained for traffic," the journal stormed. "As a matter of fact they guarantee only in effect a certain amount of traffic in the event of the bridge being completed and, like smart men of business, they quietly transfer all the risks and responsibilities to the shoulders of the unsuspecting country parson and his companions."

The Times did not escape the magazine's censure either. Although letters had been written to the editor opposing the scheme they were never published, but merely referred to and refuted with assertions that Parliament had approved the design and checked that the bridge would be safe.

The Times had also argued that the experience gained on the Tay Bridge would afford a basis on which the cost of the Forth Bridge could be worked out accurately. "It is not a little remarkable", thundered *Engineering* in reply, "that none of the best known bridge builders of the country were engaged as contractors, and it is a fact that at least one such firm had been applied to and declined the responsibility, despite the singularly advantageous terms upon which it was offered."

A week later the journal was attacking again: "It cannot be too much regretted that so little opportunity has hitherto been afforded of criticizing the design and detail of this important work, as well as the proposed mode of erection." Then "to widen the field of discussion" *Engineering* printed full details of Bouch's design, and alternative schemes.

While the public gossiped and the Press wrangled the directors of the Forth Bridge Company agreed that the foundations should be proceeded with as rapidly as possible and, when this news leaked out, over 200 men turned up at South Queensferry in search of work in a single week-end. "They were of course disappointed, as a month or two must elapse before the preparatory arrangements can be completed," it was explained.

As part of these "preparatory arrangements" a field above the Hawes Inn was laid off for the building of a huge workshop and a railway siding. Once again there had to be an official inaugural ceremony, and at this Mr. Brownhill of Inverkeithing cut the first turf, and Miss Baxter of Newhalls wheeled away the first barrowful of earth and "tipped" it. "A few appropriate remarks on the importance of the undertaking" by Mr. Brownhill completed the ceremony.

Across the river a brickworks was set up at Inverkeithing to make use of local deposits of clay.

It was evident that the company was still determined to build its bridge, but public opinion was now approaching boiling point. The Tay disaster inquiry was resumed at Dundee in late February, and then in London on 19 April, and the evidence unfolded a story of incompetence, carelessness, ignorance, and appallingly bad workmanship. Henry Abel Noble, the inspector of the bridge, described how he found slits in the iron columns of four piers, and how when he reported the matter to Bouch the columns were strapped with bands of iron. Then he told how cracks appeared in the masonry, how the tide was found to have scoured the riverbed at the bases of the columns, and how parts of the ironwork had worked themselves loose. The negligence in casting the iron at the special foundry set up at Wormit could scarcely be believed, and Scotland fumed at complaints of trains travelling over the bridge faster than the limit laid down by the Government inspector.

Throughout this Thomas Bouch was on trial just as if he stood before the High Court of Edinburgh or the Old Bailey.

In June 1880, the commissioners presented their reports on the disaster and, while William H. Barlow and Colonel William Yolland couched their verdict in gentler, general terms which protected Bouch, the third commissioner, Henry C. Rothery, spared no one. "The conclusion to which we have come," wrote Rothery, "is that this bridge was badly designed, badly constructed and badly maintained, and that its downfall was due to inherent defects in the structure which must sooner or later have brought it down. For these defects, both in the design, the construction, and the maintenance Sir Thomas Bouch is, in our opinion, mainly to blame."

As the cry went up for criminal proceedings to be taken against him, Thomas Bouch retired to his home at Moffat to die. Even before the disaster he looked older than his fifty-eight years, but now he was a prematurely senile, ailing man. Towards the end of October he caught a cold, and, having no resistance, died within a few days. He was the last victim of his bridge.

Shortly after Thomas Bouch returned to Moffat, *Engineering* announced that "for some unexplained reason" work on the Forth Bridge was at a standstill, and that almost all the hands at the brickworks at Inverkeithing and the South Queensferry workshops had been paid off. A month later the company cancelled the contracts and abandoned the project.

The "unexplained reason" was partly public opinion and partly uncertainty of the regulations which the Board of Trade might decide to lay down, especially regarding wind pressure. Barlow, Harrison, and Hawkshaw thought these might add an astronomic figure to the cost, or indeed, that the Board of Trade might even let them complete the bridge and then refuse to sanction its opening to the public. They therefore declined to approve the design or even to suggest alterations—so far as they were concerned the Forth Bridge just was not a valid proposition on any terms, and the only thing to do was abandon it.

The engineering world of 1880 had no time to mourn long for the Tay Bridge or the lives it had claimed. So far as it was concerned the matter had been investigated, the causes found, and there was no reason why the bridge should not be rebuilt—quickly. In the eighteen months of its existence the Tay Bridge had proved its worth to the North British, and its loss was a serious blow to traffic.

A scheme for rebuilding the bridge was hurriedly prepared by Sir James Brunlees, the noted Scottish engineer, and the company petitioned the House of Commons to dispense with Standing Orders and let it introduce a Bill for the rebuilding before the Session ended. Parliament agreed to consider this Bill, which was for a lower structure carried on extra piers, but when the Bill came up for its Second Reading it was violently opposed by some Members.

"What the House has now to consider," said one, "is whether it will allow the very parties who were to blame to come up before the House in the last month of the Session and endeavour to rush through Parliament a new Bill, not for the construction of a new bridge by new engineers, but for the patching up of this miserable old structure according to plans and specifications by Sir Thomas Bouch."

The Member for Perth, who wanted the Bill thrown out and brought back for its second reading in three months time, asserted that Bouch had actually signed the specifications, but this was denied by the President of the Board of Trade, who told the Commons that the ailing engineer would neither sign the plans, nor be responsible for them.

Opponents of the new Bill had their way, and it was remitted to a committee of seven members to report "as to whether the Tay Bridge should be rebuilt in its present position, or whether there is any situation more suitable," and also to consider the best height and safest way of constructing it.

This committee advised that the scheme should not be sanctioned, although it did consider that part of the river the most suitable site. However, it would be safer if the bridge were built on new foundations, and lowered slightly. The committee added the sensible comment that it might make the passage of the Parliamentary Bill for the new bridge easier if the plans were first of all shown to two or three independent engineers.

The promoters took the advice of the committee and sent for William Barlow, who was now President of the Institution of Civil Engineers and standing securely on the topmost rung of the engineering ladder. Barlow studied the old bridge, but rejected the idea of rebuilding it. Instead, he drew up plans for a completely new one 60 feet upstream, and a Bill for this was deposited in time for the 1881 Session.

If the sponsors hoped that Barlow would overawe the critics they were wrong—feeling ran high throughout the country, and in Dundee, the area most closely concerned, a low bridge with a swing opening in the centre was favoured.

And while Dundee championed the lower bridge, Perth stood out against it. As the dispute developed between the two towns the President of the Board of Trade, Joseph Chamberlain, was waited on in February 1881 by a deputation as powerful as Dundee could muster. It included a number of peers and "a whole host" of M.P.s from all parts of the north-east. A week later Perth's deputation was received, but it was a ragged affair reinforced with no more than a couple of Members of Parliament. Chamberlain heard both deputations but promised nothing, except that the Tay would be bridged again.

The North British was prepared to lower the height of the bridge, and actually prepared plans and submitted them to Parliament, but the Commons refused to waive Standing Orders as it had done for the company's Bill before, so the North British was faced with the choice of going ahead with Barlow's plans or of doing nothing for a further twelve months. Delay was the last thing the company wanted, so it decided to drop the new scheme and let the Bill for Barlow's bridge go through. It was a considerable victory for Perth.

With a number of eminent engineers, including Sir John Hawkshaw, coming forward to give evidence in favour of

102

Barlow's design, the New Tay Viaduct Bill was passed and received the Royal Assent in July 1881.

Barlow said in evidence before the Standing Orders Committee at Westminster that he proposed to test every cylinder foundation for the piers, but a clause was actually inserted to make this compulsory—Parliament was taking no chances on promised care being forgotten when building operations begun.

The M.P.s inserted another clause which, by its vagueness, caused considerable delay. This stated that the ruins of the old bridge should be removed, but it did not specify whether this had to be done before or after the new bridge was built.

The Board of Trade wanted every vestige of the broken bridge removed before work on the new one was begun, but Barlow's plans had been made on the assumption that the old structure would be left so that its girders could be transferred to the new piers as they were built. To agree to the Board of Trade's demand would add greatly to the cost, and it took a year's wrangling before a compromise was reached, and the bridge was begun.

The contractor was William Arrol, who had lost his contract for the Forth Bridge at the end of 1880. The first year was taken up with preparations, and the foundations in the river were only begun on 6 July 1883. For four years thereafter great gangs of men—as many as 900 at times—worked night and day until the bridge was completed in June 1887. To satisfy the Government inspectors sixteen engines weighing a total of 955 tons were borrowed from the North British and run over the bridge. It stood up to the test, and the public were able to travel across the Tay once more.

By the time the Tay Bridge was completed the Forth was well on the way to being bridged, although in the dark days after the 1879 disaster it had looked as if it might be a generation or more before an engineer would have the courage to span the Queensferry.

While the Bill for the new Tay Bridge was being prepared in the latter part of 1880, the Forth Bridge promoters were also working on a Bill—to give their project a decent burial. The half-yearly meeting, held on 13 January 1881, was something of a wake at which the chairman of the company and shareholders keened for the loss of their bridge and much of their money.

The chairman related the inevitability of events—how they could not know what restrictions the Board of Trade might impose, what allowance for wind pressure might have to be made, or what great parapets might be insisted on to keep trains from falling over the side of the bridge. After hearing the evidence of the Tay disaster inquiry, he believed that there was little chance of any design satisfying the Board of Trade. They had no choice but to annul the contracts and compensate the firms concerned, and if anyone considered that a waste of money he should remember that if they completed the bridge the Board of Trade might refuse to let them open it to the public, or insist on alterations which would cost far more than the amount they had already spent.

The lament contained a comparison of the dimensions of the structure with landmarks the shareholders knew, and it ended with a plea to permit the directors to push their abandonment Bill through Parliament.

The shareholders keened their accord, and *Herapath's Railway Journal* wrote an epitaph: "We are not surprised that the project is given up. The Tay Bridge disaster was enough to strike terror into the hearts of ordinary shareholders in such an undertaking."

While the abandonment Bill was before Parliament the three English companies began to have second thoughts about losing so excellent a route to the north of Scotland. Surely there must be some way of achieving a Forth crossing, and of winning some of the lucrative Scottish traffic from the Caledonian and West Coast Railways. They ordered their engineers to investigate the matter and submit their views, which proved so encouraging that the chairmen of the companies agreed to meet in York and discuss the bridge.

In a single evening a simple heads of agreement was drawn up, under which they would not pay 6 per cent on their traffic over the bridge as under the old agreement for Bouch's bridge, but instead would offer a permanent guarantee of 4 per cent whether the bridge stood or fell. On the strength of this basis of agreement the *Daily Chronicle* announced that arrangements had been made to proceed with the Forth Bridge. It was not much of an exaggeration.

The Abandonment Bill was now through the Commons and ready to go to the Lords so a quick decision was needed on whether to drop it. Once again the shareholders were summoned to Edinburgh and told of the dramatic change in their fortunes. Regardless of what happened to the Forth Bridge, stand or fall, the southern railway companies guaranteed them 4 per cent instead of the large loss which the winding up of the company promised. It was a tempting offer, and they would have been foolish to refuse it.

So the Abandonment Bill was abandoned, and the Forth was to be bridged.

As the engineers of the English companies went away to perfect their plans the North British suffered a new blow. John Stirling, now seventy-one but still in control, attended his last board meeting in Edinburgh about the middle of July 1882, and then went off to his home near Dunblane. Some days later he was taken ill, and he died before the month was out.

Stirling's long reign had seen the North British fortunes vary as suddenly and as violently as the winds of the Tay valley. From nadir he had taken them to zenith, and then he had watched them crumble once more. He had seen the Tay Bridge rise and fall; he had seen the Forth bridged on paper, and that plan destroyed. But finally he had seen an Act passed for a new bridge across the Tay, and a firm decision taken to span the Forth.

On the whole he died a happy man.

CHAPTER EIGHT

"I SUPPOSE YOU TOUCH YOUR HAT TO THE CHINESE"

ON the morning when the news of the Tay Bridge collapse broke in London two men met at an exhibition of Holbein paintings, and, if he did not actually say so, one of them was certainly in a position to say: "I told you so". He was John Fowler, an eminent engineer, whose views on the Tay Bridge were so strong that he would not permit any of his family to cross it.

Fowler was discussing the disaster with his friend James Nasmyth, inventor of the steam hammer; he pointed to the pictures in the gallery, and remarked that the bridge might be standing yet if its designer had adopted the Holbein "straddle" that attitude which the artist has given to his male figures, particularly noticeable in the picture of Henry VIII.

Fowler had the right to express an opinion on the bridge, for he was consulting engineer to the Great Northern Railway, one of the English companies interested in Bouch's Forth Bridge, which had just been begun. He was one of the three "wise men" to whom the question of bridging the Forth was referred fifteen months later when the Abandonment Bill was on its way through Parliament. The others were William Barlow, engineer to the Midland, and Thomas Harrison, engineer to the North Eastern, both of whom were already well known in connection with Bouch's Forth Bridge and the new Tay Bridge.

John Fowler was born at Wadsley Hall, near Sheffield, on 15 July 1817, and in those days when engineering was not

106

really a very respectable calling, he persuaded his father to let him become a pupil of Mr. J. T. Leather, engineer of the Sheffield Waterworks. Fowler arrived in London in 1838, just when agitation for an underground railway was beginning, and he became deeply involved. When an Act was finally obtained and this railway built Fowler was its engineer. The opening of the Metropolitan Railway, the first underground, in 1863, and its success—in spite of many eminent opinions to the contrary—set the seal of success on John Fowler's career.

The sixties were among the busiest years of his life—during that time he worked on extensions to the Metropolitan Railway, he engineered the Metropolitan District Railway, the Oswestry and Dolgelly line, the Bristol and Clifton Railway, Liverpool Central Station, the Glasgow and City Railway, a viaduct over the Clyde, St. Enoch's Station, Glasgow, Millwall Docks, railways in Devon and Cheshire, and he advised on bridges in Regent's Park and over the Serpentine. On top of all this he was elected President of the Institution of Civil Engineers, until then the youngest man to receive the honour.

In later years Fowler was involved in many huge projects at home and abroad, but undoubtedly the greatest of all, and his memorial, is the Forth Railway Bridge.

In 1861, Fowler met a young engineer who had just made up his mind to go to India, but whose promise was so apparent that Fowler persuaded him to remain in London and help with the building of the Metropolitan Railway. The offer was a tempting one, and the young man accepted it—it was the beginning of a partnership which ended only with Fowler's death in 1898. The engineer's name was Benjamin Baker.

Baker was unusual in that he was not of humble origin like so many engineers of mark. His father held a post at the ironworks at Tondu, Glamorgan, and he saw that the boy had a good education at Cheltenham Grammar School.

At the age of sixteen Baker left school and became apprenticed to H. H. Price of Neath Abbey Ironworks. Four years later, in 1860, he came to London to help in the building of Victoria Station. The following year he met Fowler and joined the great man's staff on the Metropolitan. In 1875, Baker became a partner, and the two worked together on many famous projects.

Fowler and Baker engineered a large part of London's underground—after the Metropolitan they built the St. John's Wood Railway and the District, and in later years they were consulting engineers to the first tube railway, the City and South London. After Fowler's death Baker was joint engineer to other tubes in London.

The Underground was not the sum of their achievement, however. Their work in Egypt, Ireland, America, and elsewhere, might have been enough to satisfy many another pair of engineers, but not Fowler and Baker—they went on to build the Forth Bridge, the Victorian era's greatest monument of all.

When Fowler's death ended the partnership in 1898 Baker worked on until 1907 when he died at his home near Pangbourne. He never married, and the great structures he engineered are his heirs today.

Benjamin Baker was especially interested in construction problems and the resistance of materials, and with long span bridges required for the growing railway networks, the two subjects became closely linked. In 1867 he wrote a series of articles for *Engineering* on long span bridges, and the following year another on the strength of beams, columns and arches. Four years later came a third on the strength of brickwork.

In his articles on long span bridges Baker reached the conclusion that the maximum span would necessitate the adoption of cantilevers or brackets supporting an independent girder, and in fact he and Fowler designed a bridge of this type for the Severn, but it was rejected in favour of a tunnel. When the English railway companies put the problem of bridging the Forth before their engineers in 1881, Fowler and Baker designed a bridge on this principle, with two magnificent spans of 1,710 feet.

Their "cantilever" bridge was seized upon as a great talking point among the informed, the ill-informed, and the nil informed. The term cantilever did not altogether please the bridge's creator, who said somewhat testily: "When I was a student a girder bridge which had a top member in tension and the bottom member in compression over the piers, was called a continuous girder bridge. The Forth Bridge is of that type, and I used to call it a continuous girder bridge; but the Americans persisted in calling all the bridges they were building on the same plan 'cantilever bridges'."

Baker had to bend to popular parlance and call his bridge a cantilever one.

To understand the principle of the bridge the public were asked to imagine two men trying to shake hands across a stream, but unable to reach. If one extended a stick and the other grasped it the stream would then be bridged. Similarly, the arms of the Forth bridge's cantilevers would stretch outwards to be linked by the connecting girders.

The principle was as old as the hills, and could be seen in almost every Victorian home—on a willow pattern plate. It had been adopted successfully in India, too, where a bridge across the Sutlej river at a place called Wangto was based on the principle.

"The width to be crossed here is 120 feet," *The Illustrated London News* reported of the Wangto bridge, "a large space to be bridged over by a people who are still in the most primitive condition of civilization, and to whom mechanical engineering as a science is totally unknown."

Elsewhere in the Orient, and in North America, too, cantilever bridges had been built, but it was the willow pattern version that caught the public imagination, and the principle was firmly associated with China in most minds. To an engineer Lady Napier of Magdala said, "I suppose you touch your hat to the Chinese."

"Yes, indeed," he replied, "bridges on that principle were built in China many centuries ago."

Lady Napier's remark was no more fatuous than many made by more knowledgeable people over the decade following publication of the Fowler-Baker plan. Yet it was vital for the public's questions to be answered with care and patience, for understanding of the design would inspire confidence in the bridge when the railway traveller came to use it.

Baker had a human model devised for lectures, and the

description of this was reproduced—as one admiring writer put it—"in every language of the civilized globe".

For this two men sat on chairs and extended their arms, which they supported by grasping sticks abutting against the chairs. This represented the two double cantilevers. The central beam was represented by a short stick slung from the near hands of the two men, and the human cantilevers were anchored by ropes extending from the men's other hands to a pile of bricks. When stresses were brought to bear on this system by a load on the central beam, the ropes came into tension and the sticks and chair legs into compression.

The "stress" brought to bear on Baker's human model was Kaichi Watanabe, a Japanese student of Messrs. Fowler and Baker, whose presence reminded everybody of the debt the designers owed to the Far East.

In the Forth Bridge one had to imagine the chairs placed a third of a mile apart, the men's heads 340 feet above ground, the pull on each arm about 4,000 tons, the thrust of each stick over 6,000 tons, and the weight on the legs of the chair about 25,000 tons. It all added up to a fantastic scheme which the public could only marvel at and the engineering world study with astonished admiration.

To help the public to comprehend the inmensity of the bridge, it was compared with landmarks which they knew. Said *The Illustrated London News*:

"The whole length of the viaduct is 8,296 feet, which is over a mile and a half. A portion of this, about five-eighths of a mile, connects the bridge proper with the high ground on each side of the firth. The bridge itself is 5,349 feet 9 inches in length, which is about 60 feet over a mile.

"It may perhaps give the best idea of size by taking a like along a well-known thoroughfare in London. From Charing Cross along the Strand and Fleet Street to the foot of Ludgate Hill is over a mile, and would be a little longer than the bridge. From Marble Arch along Oxford Street to Berners Street, which is only a little west of Tottenham Court Road, is exactly a mile: add 60 feet more, and there is the length of the Forth Bridge".

Of the 1,710 feet span it said: "This long stride over space will be grasped better by the mind, when it is stated that it is about the same distance as that between Charing Cross Station and Somerset House."

Diagrams compared its height with every structure of importance in the world, and only the Great Pyramid, Cologne Cathedral and old St. Paul's surpassed it.

The two great spans of the bridge were each 1,710 feet long, with another two to shoreward of 675 feet each, all resting on three massive piers set on the Fife shore, on Inchgarvie, and on the edge of the shelf off South Queensferry. Each of these piers consisted of four circular columns of Arbroath stone faced with Aberdeen granite. The piers were 36 feet high and tapered from a diameter of 53 feet at the bottom to 49 feet at the top. In each were 48 steel bolts $2\frac{1}{2}$ inches in diameter, and 24 feet long to hold down the superstructure.

The superstructure of one of the spans weighed in the region of 16,000 tons, compared with the 800 tons or so which was the greatest load they would be likely to carry. In fact wind pressure was a more dangerous factor than was the weight of trains crossing the bridge. To resist wind the structure was tapered to straddle the piers, the columns being 120 feet apart at the point where they stood on the piers and only 33 feet apart at the top. The bottom members of the cantilevers similarly widened out at the piers.

The Board of Trade was concerned about wind pressure too, and insisted that 56 pounds per square foot should be allowed for. In fact the greatest pressure recorded by wind gauges on Inchgarvie during construction was 20 pounds per square foot.

Baker was confident that his bridge could stand up to any wind. "All of the structure is thoroughly braced together by wind bracing of lattice girders so that a hurricane or cyclone storm may blow in any direction, up or down the Forth without affecting the stability of the bridge," he said. "Indeed, even if a hurricane were blowing up one side of the Forth and down the other, tending to rotate the cantilevers on the piers, the bridge has the strength to resist such a combination."

To reduce weight and yet retain maximum strength the main compression members were hollow tubes of steel—the tube of a cantilever 12 feet in diameter and of steel one-and-a-quarter inches thick, and it would be subject to an end pressure of 2,282 tons from the deadweight, 1,022 tons from the trains, and 2,920 tons from the wind—a total of 6,224 tons, which Baker compared with the weight of one of the largest transatlantic liners of the day filled with cargo. The vertical tube was to be 343 feet high, 12 feet in diameter, and almost five-eighths of an inch thick. Its load could total 3,279 tons.

So large a mass of metal was, of course, liable to great expansion and contraction as the temperature changed from season to season and even day to day, and this had to be allowed for. Strictly speaking the central girders and the cantilevers were not joined, but had special expansion joints to allow for shrinkage and expansion. The extreme variation was calculated not to exceed 9 inches, but nevertheless double was allowed for.

That, then, was the bridge which Fowler and Baker laid before the English railway companies, and which was taken up with such enthusiasm. At ten o'clock on the morning of Friday, 30 September 1881, the chairman and managers of the English companies and the North British met in Edinburgh, and discussed the design with their engineers. All were agreed that the Fowler-Baker plan was the solution to their problem, and in the course of the following two hours they instructed that a Parliamentary Bill for the bridge should be drafted in time for the new Session.

When the talking was over the party then went off on a junket through Fife to study routes which would make the maximum use of their bridge. A special train conveyed them to South Queensferry, the *John Beaumont* ferried them to Fife, and another train took them to Mawcarse, where they picnicked on the platform. Luncheon over, as many as could be accommodated in a brake set out on a drive through Glenfarg to prospect for a railway to Bridge of Earn—a line for which the North British had actually obtained an Act in 1863. The special train took those who could not find room in the brake to Bridge of Earn by way of Ladybank, and the two parties met up again at 3.30. The return journey was by Ladybank and Burntisland, and Edinburgh was reached at six o'clock.

When the Bill for the bridge came before Parliament there was little real opposition to it as the Government's inspecting officers had discussed the design with Fowler and Baker. A 13-foot model of the bridge was used to dispose of much opposition evidence, and this caused such interest that it was put on show at the House of Commons afterwards.

One point at issue was the reluctance of the Board of Trade to agree to have its inspectors at the site throughout construction, but eventually it compromised and accepted responsibility for quarterly inspections.

That was enough to satisfy most opponents of the Bill, and its passage from there on was smooth. It received the Royal Assent on 12 July 1882.

In November the contracts were let out to Sir Thomas Tancred, T. H. Falkiner, and Joseph Phillips, of London, and to William Arrol, who was already busy on the new Tay Bridge. The price was to be £1,600,000 which was within a few thousand pounds of the engineers' parliamentary estimate, and the time of construction was to be five years.

While the contractors prepared to begin operations the critics were busy. Sir George Airey, the former Astronomer Royal, who had advised Bouch so doubtfully on wind pressures while he was designing the bridge of 1873, wrote in an article that a suspension bridge would be much better, and that "we may reasonably expect the destruction of the Forth Bridge in a lighter gale than that which destroyed the Tay Bridge".

The *Newbury News* carried confused thinking a stage further by printing a paragraph on the letting of the contracts: "The well-known firm of Messrs. Falkiner and Tancred of London, in conjunction with Messrs. Arrol of Glasgow, have obtained the contracts for the building of the Forth Bridge, better known as the Tay Bridge, the disaster to which created such a sensation throughout the country."

The *Newbury News* was just wrong and could be ignored, but could Sir George Airey? Although he was now over eighty he was still an important personage in the world of science, and his criticisms could not be ignored.

Engineering took a delight in refuting the old man's opinions, and reminding its readers of similar gaffes he had committed—how, for example, he had expressed the opinion at the time of the Great Exhibition of 1851 that the Crystal Palace was liable to fall down.

"Sir George Airey's periodic attacks on engineering works are instructive inasmuch as they serve to indicate the blunders which inexperienced engineers would be likely to fall into if entrusted with responsibility before being properly qualified," commented *Engineering*. "The late Astronomer Royal throughout his long career has laboured under the hallucination that the science of engineering is not a matter of experience and research, but of intuition. . . .

"Possibly he may have at times mistaken the silence of engineers for acquiescence, but supposing Sir George wrote a letter stating that in his opinion the distance from London to Edinburgh was twenty miles, we doubt whether anyone would take the trouble to correct him."

In the face of this, and scorn from a number of other engineers, Sir George was demolished.

In December 1882, several hundred workmen arrived at Queensferry to begin work on the bridge. Time would tell if there was any truth in Sir George's opinions.

CHAPTER NINE

A CREDIT TO ALL

FOR William Arrol the site at South Queensferry was familiar; it was here that he had broken ground three years earlier, and the derelict sheds were reminders of that occasion. The first task was to put these mouldering workshops into order, and install new equipment.

South Queensferry was the principal base for the construction of the bridge, for it was near the main Edinburgh–Glasgow railway, and had a branch line running right to it. Eventually more than sixty acres were covered with huge workshops, stores, houses for workmen, yards and railway sidings. When the equipment outgrew the site extra space was taken beyond the railway and two bridges made from girders of the old Tay Bridge were built over the track to link the sections.

A long wooden jetty was built in the shallow water off the southern shore, and this eventually stretched nearly half a mile out into the firth. A railway was built on it, and joined to the Queensferry branch by a 65-foot bridge. On a section of this line where the gradient was steep a stationary engine hauled the trucks up from the jetty. This pier was, of course, used also for unloading materials for the construction work, and by the contractors' little fleet of vessels which plied across the firth. To the east of the site of the bridge, slipways were erected to launch the giant caissons for the piers.

The latest inventions were used to speed the works—a telephone line was laid across the river, and electric light was used to enable the men to carry on with the job at night. Later on electricity proved inadequate and a form of incandescent lighting was adopted.

On the northern bank the old coastguard station was demolished to make way for the piers of the Fife cantilever, and the old ferry slipway was enlarged. Here, too, homes were built for the workmen.

Slowly construction was getting under way.

On Thursday, 6 June 1893, a ceremony was held just to the east of the church at North Queensferry, when Sir Thomas Tancred laid the first granite block with full masonic honours.

A week later the Board of Trade inspectors, C. S. Hutchinson and F. A. Marindin, presented their first quarterly report. It contained little news of progress on the permanent parts of the bridge, but it did promise excellent workmanship. "Preparations indicate that it is the intention of the engineers and contractors to carry out the works in a manner suitable to the magnitude of the undertaking," they wrote.

In the next report there was more definite progress—foundations of a number of piers for the approach spans were in, and the stonework was beginning to rise. To the sightseer a vestige of a bridge was now apparent, and even the little which could be seen was impressive.

The temporary works were proceeding well, too. On the southern shore an enormous amount of staging had been erected, and workmen's houses, a large canteen, and a reading room were ready. Inchgarvie's landing stage was nearly complete, and part of the rock had been levelled to hold materials. An iron bridge joined the two sections of the island to make building work easier. In Fife a great iron staging had been completed on the site of the piers for the cantilever, and diamond drills were poised ready to tear into the heart of the rock to provide secure foundations.

On the river the builders had a fleet of eight barges, a steam barge, a steam tug, and a steam launch in service already, and with more expected any day.

Forty thousand cubic feet of granite waited on the shore to be built into the piers, and the great 24-foot long holding-down bolts had been delivered. Immense as this may seem, the work—the real building of the bridge—was only beginning. The four enormous piers to support each of the three cantilevers had yet to be begun, and these alone would entail several years' difficult work.

For the foundations under water cofferdams or caissons had to be built to enclose an area in which the water could be pumped out so that the workmen could prepare the foundations. In full cofferdams, or dams as they were usually called, the water is permanently excluded, but in half-tide dams the water enters at each high tide and has to be pumped out again. Sometimes these caissons were closed in at the top like a bell, and these were called pneumatic caissons.

Addressing the Royal Institution in 1887 Baker described the laying of the foundations of these piers. Of those on the north side of the estuary he said:

"The rock was blasted into steps, diamond drills being used. Even this comparatively simple work was not executed without considerable trouble, as the sloping rock bottom was covered with a closely compacted mass of boulders and rubbish, through which the water flowed into the dam in almost unmanageable quantity. After many months' work the water was sufficiently excluded by the use of cement bags and liquid grout poured in by divers under water and other expedients, and concrete foundations and masonry were proceeded with."

Pneumatic caissons were used for the southernmost piers of the Inchgarvie cantilever. Here the rocky bottom was sloping and irregular, and the water at high tide was 72 feet deep. Baker said of it:

"Two wrought iron caissons, which might be likened to large tubs or buckets 70 feet in diameter and 50 to 60 feet high, were built on launching ways on the sloping southern foreshore of the Forth. The bottom of each caisson was set up seven feet above the cutting edge, and so constituted a chamber 70 feet in diameter and 7 feet high, capable of being filled at the proper time with compressed air to enable the men to work, as in a diving bell, below the water of the Forth.

"The caisson weighed about 470 tons, was launched, and

117

then taken to a berth alongside the Queensferry jetty, where a certain amount of concrete, brickwork and staging was added, bringing the weight up to 2,640 tons. At Inchgarvie a very strong and costly staging had previously been erected alongside which the caisson was finally moored in correct position for sinking. While the work described was proceeding divers and labourers were engaged in making a level bed for the caisson to sit on. The 16-foot slope in the rock bottom was levelled up by bags filled with sand or concrete. As soon as the weight of the caisson and filling reached 3,270 tons the caisson rested on the sandbags and floated no more.

"The high ledge of rock upon which the northerly edge of the caisson rested was blasted away, holes being driven by rock drills and otherwise under the cutting edge and about six inches beyond for the charges. After the men had gained a little experience in this work no difficulty was found in undercutting the hard whinstone rock to allow the edge of the caisson to sink, and of course there was still less difficulty in removing the sandbags temporarily used to form a level bed.

"The interior rock was excavated as easily as on dry land, the whole of the 70-foot diameter by 7-foot high chamber being thoroughly lighted by electricity. Access was obtained through a vertical tube with an air-lock at the top, and many visitors ventured to pass through this and look into the lighted chamber below, where the pressure at times was as high as 35 pounds per square inch.

· "Probably the most astonished visitors were some salmon, who, attracted by the commotion in the water caused by the escape of compressed air under the edge of the caisson, found themselves in the electric-lighted chamber. When in the chamber the only notice of this escape of large volumes of air was the sudden pervadence of a dense fog, but outside a huge wave of aerated water would rise above the level of the sea, and a general effect prevail of something terrible going on below. No doubt the salmon thought they had come to a cascade turned upside down, and following their instinct of heading up it, met their fate."

Another visitor whose surprise was as great as that of the

salmon, but who escaped their fate, was a man who took a flask of whisky into the chamber with him and treated the men to a drink after admiring the works. He replaced the empty flask in his hip pocket and climbed out of the chamber, forgetting that the flask was now full of compressed air and of course when he reached normal atmospheric pressure outside the chamber the flask exploded. He escaped injury, but learnt a valuable lesson in science.

The first of the two deep caissons in Inchgarvie was launched on 30 March 1885, and both were finished to sea level by the end of the year.

Baker described the building of the piers for the Queensferry cantilever:

"At Queensferry all four piers were founded on caissons identical in principle with those used for the deep Garvie piers. The deepest was 89 feet below high water, and weighed 20,000 tons; the shallowest of the four was 71 feet high, the diameter in all cases, as at Garvie, being 70 feet at the base. Some difference in detail occurred in these caissons, as compared with Garvie, owing to the difference of the conditions. Thus, instead of a sloping surface of rock, the bed of the Forth was of soft mud to a considerable depth, through which the caissons had to be sunk into the hard boulder clay. Double skins were provided for the caissons, between which concrete could be filled in to varying heights if necessary, so that greater weight might be applied to the cutting edge where the mud was hard than where it was soft. The annular wall of concrete also gave great strength to resist the hydrostatic pressure outside the caisson, for it must be understood that the water was excluded both below and above the working chamber.

"The process of sinking was as follows: the caisson being seated on the soft mud, which, of course, practically filled the working chamber, air was blown in, and a few men descended the shaft or tube of access to the working chamber in order to clear away the mud. This was done by diluting it to the necessary extent by water brought down a pipe under pressure, and by blowing it out in this liquid state through another pipe by means of the pressure of air in the chamber. It was found that the mud sealed the caisson, so that a pressure of air considerably in excess of that of the water outside could be kept up, and it was unnecessary to vary the pressure according to the height of the tide. In working through the soft mud both intelligence and courage were called for on the part of the men, and it is a pleasure and duty for me to say that the Italians and Belgians engaged on the work were never found wanting in those qualifications."

On New Year's Day, 1885, the north-west caisson off South Queensferry stuck in the mud just as it was being towed into position, and instead of rising with the tide, it was so weighed down with 4,000 tons of concrete that it sat where it was and became flooded. This additional water caused the caisson to sink still further into the mud, and to tilt forward. The only thing to be done now was to build up the sides of the caisson above the high tide level and then to pump out the water and refloat the caisson. This took nearly three months, and when the caisson was empty the pressure of water caused its walls to buckle, killing two men. Divers then had to make the caisson watertight again, and finally on 19 October it was floated into position and sunk.

The last of the main piers was completed in March 1886, almost exactly two years after the first caisson had been floated out.

With the piers completed it was time to begin the metal structure of the bridge. At the workshops in South Queensferry the steelwork was made and fitted.

"Multiple drills tear through immense thickness of steel at an astonishing rate," said Benjamin Baker. "The larger machines have ten drills, which, going as they do day and night at 180 revolutions per minute, perform work equivalent to boring an inch hole through 280-feet thicknesses of solid steel every twenty-four hours.

"The material used throughout is Siemens steel of the finest quality, made at the Steel Company's works in Glasgow, and Landore in South Wales. Although one-and-a-half times stronger than wrought iron it is not in any sense of the word

This human model was contrived to illustrate the cantilever principle, and to emphasize its Far Eastern origin a Japanese student, Kaichi Watanabe, was used as the "stress" in the centre

The central tower of the Fife side, with the great arms of the cantilever beginning to stretch outwards

The steel framework of the bridge dwarfs the houses of North
Queensferry, the ancient ferryman's village

Opinion was divided on the artistic merit of the
piece of engineering such as

From Inchgarvie the great mass of steel reaches out over the Forth.
Soon it will meet the cantilever extending from the south

bridge, but everyone agreed that it was a superb
Scotland had never before seen

1961—the Forth is spanned again, and the two 512-foot towers of the road bridge have already risen from the river. This view is from the southern shore. *(Below)* End of 1962—the cables are now completed and the first of the decking suspenders are slung from them

brittle, as steel is often popularly supposed to be, but it is tough and ductile as copper. You can fold half-inch plates like newspapers and tie rivet bars like twine into knots."

This beautiful steel was heated in great furnaces, hauled between the dies of an 800-ton hydraulic press, and bent to the proper radius. When cooled the edges were planed, and the plates built up to form a tube. In the drilling yard, holes were made for the rivets and the plates were then dismantled, cleaned, and stacked ready for erection.

Erection was not easy as the depth of water and exposed situation made it impossible to erect scaffolding. "The principle was therefore to build first the portion of the superstructure over the main piers," said Baker. "The great steel towers as they may be called, although really parts of the cantilever, and to add successive bays of the cantilever right and left of the towers, and therefore balancing each other, until the whole is complete. This being the general principle, a great deal yet remained to be done in settling the details."

"Settling the details" was no simple matter either, and Baker has left us a full description.

"After the skewbacks, horizontal tubes, and a certain length of verticals, as high as steam cranes could conveniently reach were built, a lifting stage was erected. This consisted of two platforms, one on each side of the bridge and four hydraulic lifting rams, one in each 12-foot tube. To carry these rams, cross girders were fitted in the tubes, capable of being raised so as to support the rams and platforms as erection proceeded, and steel pins were slipped in to hold the cross girder. Travelling cranes, with the men working aloft, are of course, raised with the platforms when hydraulic pressure is let into the ram. The mode of procedure is to raise the platform one foot, and slip in the steel pins to carry the load, whilst the rams are getting ready to make another stroke of one foot. When a 16-foot lift had been so made, which is a matter of a few hours, a pause of some two or three days occurs to allow the riveting to be completed. The advance at times has been at the rate of three lifts, or 48 feet in height in a week.

121

"The riveting appliances designed by Mr. Arrol are of a very special and even formidable character, each machine weighing about sixteen tons. It consists essentially of an inside and outside hydraulic ram mounted on longitudinal and annular girders in such a manner as to command every rivet in the tubes and to close the same by hydraulic pressure. Pipes from the hydraulic pumps are carried up inside the tubes to the riveters, and oil furnaces for heating the rivets are placed in convenient spots also inside the tubes. By practice and the stimulus of premiums the men have succeeded in putting in 800 rivets per day with one of the machines at a height of 300 feet above the sea, which in fact, is more than they accomplished when working at ground level. Indeed, by the system of erection adopted, the element of height is practically annihilated, and with ordinary caution the men are safer aloft than below, as in the former case they are not liable to have things dropped on their head."

That, then, is how the central towers were built. Next came the bays of the cantilevers, and once again the men improvized as the job progressed. "We thought at first that the crane men and erectors would require practically to be close together," wrote Baker, "but we have found out, or rather the men have found out for themselves, that cranes 370 feet up in the air can handle work at ground level, and that the long steel wire ropes hanging from the crane jibs, instead of being destructive of their usefulness, are often of great advantage, as plates and bars can be swung out pendulum fashion to a distance far beyond the reach of the jib itself. The result of experience, combined with the boldness of the men, enables us to dispense with the use of lifting platforms for the outer bays of the cantilevers, and in lieu of this mode of erection to use steam cranes travelling on the top."

As the great cantilevers grew upward and outward the girders to carry the permanent way were put in so that they furnished an extra platform from which more of the work could be done. These girders were so strong that they could project a hundred feet over the firth and still bear the weight of a three-ton crane and its load at their tip.

The cantilevers completed, lastly came the linking central girders. These could not be hoisted up from the river because of currents, the exposed position of the bridge, and the expansion and contraction of so large a mass of metal due to changes in temperature.

In September 1889, Baker wrote, "Almost every engineering visitor to the works during the past years has asked, 'How are you going to erect the central girder?' I have never varied myself in opinion as to what would be the best way of doing the work. In a paper read before the British Association at Southampton in 1882, or seven years ago, I said, 'The central girder will be erected on the overhanging system, temporary connection being formed between the ends of the cantilevers and central girders. The closing lengths of key pieces at the centre of each 1,700-foot span will be put in on a cloudy day or at night, when there is little variation of temperature, and the details will be arranged that the key-piece can be completed and the temporary connections cut away in a few hours, so as to avoid any temporary inconvenience from changes of temperature."

The last girder was finally joined on 14 November 1889. "The north central girder had in the meantime been built out in precisely similar manner, and by 15 October it was sufficiently advanced to allow a gangway 65 feet long to be laid across. This enabled the directors of the company to walk across the bridge from end to end, the chairman of the company being actually the first person to cross the north span.

"By 28 October the last booms were put in, and by 6 November everything was ready to connect the girder also. The temperature on that day did not rise, however, sufficiently high to make the joint but in the night a sudden rise took place, and by 7.30 in the morning the bottom booms were joined together for good.

"It now required a good fall of the temperature to get the top booms connected, for the two halves of this girder had been set less high at starting, and there was now practically no camber in the bottom booms. But the weather remained obstinate, and the temperature very high, and it was not until the morning of 14 November that the key plates could be driven in, and the final connection made.

"An episode of which much has been made in the papers, occurred on this occasion, and the facts are simply as follows. After the wedges at the bottom ends had been drawn out and the key-plates driven in, a slight rise of temperature was indicated by the thermometer in the course of the morning, and orders were given to remove the bolts in the central joints of the connecting ties and to light the furnaces. Whether the thermometer indicated wrongly or whether a decrease of the same took place, it is not now possible to prove, but when only about thirty-six of the turned steel bolts remained in the joints and before the furnaces could get fairly started, the plate-ties sheared the remaining bolts and parted with a bang like a shot from a 38-ton gun.

"Something of a shake occurred in the cantilevers, which was felt at the opposite ends and caused some little commotion among the men. No mishap occurred, however, and nothing in the way of a fall of the girders took place as stated in the papers, simply the work of the furnaces and the task of knocking out thirty-six bolts was saved, and the girder swung on its rockers as freely as if it had been freed in the most natural manner."

Completion of the linking girders did not mean that the bridge was ready, not by any means. It was to take another four months before the first traveller was to cross by train to Fife.

Construction had grossly overrun the estimates both in time and money, and the burden it had put upon the men who built it can hardly be calculated.

John Fowler was already an old man when the bridge was begun, and throughout its construction he suffered from bronchial trouble which forced him to seek better health abroad from time to time.

In the spring of 1884 he wrote to his wife from Barcelona: "I sometimes analyse my motives in coming to Spain. The ostensible motive, of course, is to see Per's (his son's) work at the Lomo de Bas mines, as to which I have special duties as chairman, but I think the strongest of all is to endeavour to see the Forth Bridge finished, and to have a few more birthdays with you."

Fowler returned and drove himself harder than ever in order to drive the contractors harder, and occasionally his correspondence revealed a pathetic gratitude for a small victory in his battle against illness. "The air is softer with the rain," he wrote as winter of 1886 came on, "and probably my cough will be less troublesome than it was with the cold of yesterday and the day before. I should be pleased if I could safely and with reasonable comfort remain in England all the winter, and spend much of my time here. We must see."

By the time the bridge was completed he was aged, and subject to severe attacks of bronchitis; his breathing became more difficult throughout the eight years of life that remained to him.

Fowler's partner, Benjamin Baker, was only forty-two when he began the task of spanning the Queensferry, but the ceaseless worry and strain made him an old man before it was finished. Yet he was still only fifty. Baker was the voice of the builders. He began with an address to the British Association in 1882, and from then on he talked frequently and well on the subject. Scarcely a B.A. meeting passed without an address by him, and it is largely due to these papers and similar ones to other bodies that we know so much of the detailed work of the bridge builders.

William Arrol was just a year older than Benjamin Baker, and, like Baker and Fowler, he was an old man when the bridge was handed over to the owners. As contractor he had the day-to-day task of finding ways of doing the work; he had to design machinery to suit particular tasks; and he had to watch like a father over the thousands of men at work on the site. Typical of the ingenuity of Arrol is the hydraulic riveting machine which he designed to speed the job of inserting the seven million rivets in the steelwork.

During the period of building Fowler and Baker had three resident engineers—Allan Stewart, P. W. Meik (1883-86), and F. E. Cooper (1886-90). Thomas Scott was the contractors' manager, and W. Westhofen, who wrote a superb description of the building of the bridge for *Engineering*, was in charge at Inchgarvie. On shore the sixty acres of workshops, yards, and drawing offices were in the charge of A. S. Biggart.

These were the officers. What of the army of "briggers", as those who worked on the construction of the Forth Bridge became known? The job required men not only of skill but of courage, and as the wages were high, it is not surprising that all sorts of men drifted to the ferry in search of employment. While the "briggers" were about crime rose in the neighbouring towns—week-ends were wild and each Monday morning brought a parade of wrongdoers before the Justices of the Peace. Fines were heavy, and the "briggers" subscribed to a fund to pay them, and to provide a retainer for a lawyer who would defend them.

These men were doing a job which they knew few had the courage to tackle, and this gave them a swagger as they paraded the streets of the towns to the north and south of the ferry. Local people recognized them by their bell-bottom trousers and the large rings made from Forth Bridge steel which they flaunted on their fingers.

But it would be unfair to the "briggers" to remember only those who made their mark by breaking the law. Many of the men were honest, law-abiding citizens who brought their families with them when they came from the industrial cities to seek employment at Queensferry. Some lived in special houses built for them at Queensferry, while others found homes at Dalmeny, Kirkliston, Inverkeithing, Dunfermline, and other towns and villages around. Many stayed on afterwards, and their descendants are still there today. Not all of the workmen lived by the ferry however—workmen's trains ran from Edinburgh and Leith to South Queensferry each day, and there were special steamer services on the Forth for the men.

To the tradesmen of towns by the Queensferry, and particularly to the public-house owners, the men brought eight good years, when money was plentiful and no one seemed particularly anxious to hang on to it.

Arrol was a forward-looking man, careful of the welfare of

his men. In addition to providing temporary housing he built a reading-room and a dining-room which was used in the winter evenings for concerts. Membership of the company's Sick and Accident Club was compulsory, for Arrol realized the dangers to which the men were exposed. For fourpence a week the workers were assured of twelve shillings a week benefit in case of sickness. This fund was augmented by the contractors and the public who visited the works from time to time.

Wire netting was stretched on frames below exposed points where the men were working, and handrails were provided where possible. Nevertheless the bridge claimed fifty-seven lives during building—roughly one every six weeks. Some of these were due to foolhardiness of youths who would jump from plank to plank a hundred feet above the firth as if they were at ground level; others were due to carelessness, as when a man walked backwards into a hole he had been sent to cover; but a number of the accidents were due to the danger of working so high above an exposed river. The engineers and contractors knew the dangers which the men ran, and Baker was their spokesman:

"Speaking on behalf of the engineers, I may say that we never ask a workman to do a thing which we are not prepared to do ourselves, but of course men will on their own initiative occasionally do rash things. Thus, not long ago a man trusted himself at a great height to the simple grasp of a rope, and his hand getting numbed with cold he unconsciously relaxed his hold and fell backwards a descent of 120 feet, happily into the water from which he was fished out, little the worse, after sinking twice.

"Another man going up in a hoist the other day, having that familiarity with danger which breeds contempt, did not trouble to close the rail, and stumbling backwards fell a distance of 180 feet, carrying away a dozen rungs of a ladder with which he came into contact as if they had been straws.

"These are instances of rashness, but the best men run risks from their fellow-workmen. Thus a splendid fellow, active as a cat, who would run hand over hand along a rope at any height, was knocked over by a man dropping a wedge on him from above, and killed by a fall of between 100 and 200 feet.

"There are about 500 men at work at each main pier, and something is always dropping from aloft. I saw a hole one inch in diameter made through the four inch timber of the staging by a spanner which fell about 300 feet, and took off a man's cap in its course. On another occasion a dropped spanner entered a man's waistcoat and came out at his ankle, tearing open the whole of his clothes, but not injuring the man himself in any way."

During the early part of the work there were not the same dangers as later when hundreds of men were working in exposed positions high above the river, but even in sinking the caissons there was considerable risk of the caisson sinking suddenly and imprisoning the men. Indeed, two men were killed when water burst into the north-west caisson of the Queensferry cantilever after the mishap of New Year's Day 1885. On another occasion some of the men were buried up to their chins in mud before rescuers reached them.

As the building of the steelwork got under way, however, the number of fatal accidents rose, and the newspapers took up the cause of the men exposed to such danger. The men themselves were not averse to making capital out of these accidents, for when two men were killed and four others injured by a carelessly dropped staging on 2 June 1887 the rest promptly went on strike for danger money while working on the higher parts of the structure. One wonders if those at lower levels might not have been in the greater danger.

The Board of Trade inspectors were not satisfied that all that could was being done to prevent accidents. "We regret to have to notice that the percentage of fatal accidents to the men employed upon the works had increased, no less than seven men having lost their lives during the last quarter," they reported in 1887. It would be more than could be reasonably expected that a structure of this character could be erected without any loss of life, but it would seem that more than one of the fatal accidents during the last quarter might have been

128

averted by a more strict supervision on the part of the foreman and leading hands at the main piers.

"We ourselves noticed when on top of the North Queensferry pier, an accident due entirely to the carelessness or ignorance of a foreman; this, providentially, had no ill results, but might easily have caused loss of life."

The public agreed that more should be done to prevent accidents, and the contractors were forced in September to send a letter to the newspapers as a counterblast to the "exaggerated reports" on the number of accidents on the bridge.

"All that good appliances, safeguards, and supervision can do we try our best to maintain," wrote Messrs. Tancred, Arrol, "but we cannot successfully contend against recklessness or thoughtlessness of the men themselves."

Another couple of deaths shortly afterwards prompted Andrew Cunningham, editor of the *Dunfermline Journal*, to ask what could be done. "The monthly slaughter cannot be tolerated," wrote Cunningham, "the warnings by the Government inspectors and the contractors seem to be allowed to be blown over the cantilevers like the morning mist."

Inspectors of the quality of construction were not enough, Cunningham wanted special inspectors to investigate accidents as there were in the coalmines.

When an accident occurred the inspector would visit the scene and make an on-the-spot investigation which would enable him to submit recommendations by which a similar mishap could be avoided.

The suggestion aroused considerable discussion throughout the country and prompted Benjamin Baker to comment that in his opinion the appointment of Government inspectors would have a detrimental effect. He cited the opinions of Royal Commissions which had considered the question of accidents on several occasions, and each of which had declared that to appoint such an authority would make the Government responsible for equipment, and would interfere unduly with management.

"Despite the findings of the whole of the Royal Commissions that have sat upon any subject since the days of Cromwell, we adhere to every statement made in our issues of last week and today," retorted Cunningham.

The "slaughter" went on despite all the precautions of the contractors and engineers, and the November quarterly report recorded eight accidents, although the inspectors observed that "since our last visit very considerable additions have been made to the appliances for protection of the men employed upon all parts of the structure."

And in part, at least, they agreed with the contractors.

"It is stated that it is very difficult to persuade many of the men to adopt the most ordinary precautions, and we ourselves noticed more than one instance of what can only be characterized as foolhardiness, such as should be discountenanced and prevented in every possible way."

The fifty-seven men who died building the bridge were quickly forgotten by the public who admired the hundreds of pictures and devoured the thousands of words which filled the Press. Now all that remained was for the bridge to be tested.

Nature obligingly did this on her own on 26 January 1890, when a great gale blew along the firth, and all its fury could not budge the Forth Bridge. Then the inspectors paid their twenty-eighth and final quarterly visit to Queensferry. They examined every detail with the greatest care, and then ordered two heavy trains totalling 900 tons to pass over the bridge—causing only the most minute deflection—even less than they expected.

C. S. Hutchinson and F. A. Marindin were satisfied and wrote: "We are therefore able to report that the Forth Bridge may be safely opened for passenger traffic as soon as the approach railways have been completed."

And their final comment was fitting ending to the saga of the spanning of the Queensferry.

"In conclusion we think it right to record our opinion that this great undertaking, every part of which we have seen at different stages of its construction, is a wonderful example of thoroughly good workmanship with excellent materials and that both in its conception and in its execution it is a credit to all who have been connected with it, bearing testimony to the ability of the engineers who have designed it, to the skill and resource of those who have superintended and constructed it, and to the zeal and courage of the workmen who have been employed upon it."

That was a tribute indeed, for it came from the two men who, apart from the designers, knew the bridge best of all.

CHAPTER TEN

ART AND CRAFT

THE bridge was ready, but who was to perform the opening ceremony? Just before Christmas of 1889 a rumour was current in Edinburgh that the Prince of Wales would come to Scotland in March to do the honours, and for once rumour was right. But the Prince's train was not the first to carry passengers over the bridge—on 24 January 1890, a train was driven over the bridge and back by the Machioness of Tweeddale, wife of the Chairman of the North British Railway. Aboard it were the chairmen of two of the English companies which had made the bridge possible.

The Prince of Wales travelled north on Monday, 3 March, and stayed the night as guest of the Earl of Rosebery at Dalmeny. On the following morning he set out to drive in the last rivet and declare the bridge open. He was accompanied by Prince George, the future King George V, the Duke of Edinburgh, who had travelled from Russia especially to be present, and the Duke of Fife. A host of railway directors, Scottish nobles, Lord Provosts, and a miscellaneous collection of other notables, ranging from the Bishop of Lichfield to Monsieur Eiffel of Eiffel Tower fame, completed the guest list.

At the Forth Bridge Station, Fowler, Baker, Phillips and Arrol met the royal train and boarded it to explain the detail of the bridge to the Prince as he was taken across it. At North Queensferry the royal party went aboard a steamer and sailed under the great belly of the bridge, round Inchgarvie, across the firth, and then back to the northern shore to rejoin the train.

In the middle of the north connecting girder the train stopped, and the Prince of Wales stepped out into the icy wind which was blowing strongly down the firth, and drove in the last of the seven million rivets used in the bridge. The rivet was gilded and bore the inscription: "Last rivet put in by H.R.H. the Prince of Wales". Two men hidden from sight below the permanent way manipulated the hydraulic riveter, and the Marquis of Tweeddale handed the Prince a silver key with which the job was done.

At the south cantilever another platform had been erected and the Prince once more left the train. It was now half-past one and bitterly cold, so the Prince braced himself, shouted into the wind, "Ladies and Gentlemen, I now declare the Forth Bridge open," and thankfully re-entered the train. It was time for lunch.

The engineers' model room at South Queensferry had been handsomely disguised as a banqueting hall, and here the guests sat down to eat at two o'clock. Crimson, gold, and rose material covered the walls, and the roof was hidden by strips of white calico edged with red and blue. Over the head table hung a magnificent canopy of crimson and gold plush, with the royal arms and the Prince of Wales's motto on a gold scroll. Shields bearing the arms of towns in England and Scotland and of the great railway companies were ranged along the walls.

Mr. Matthew William Thompson, chairman of the Forth Bridge and Midland Railway companies, proposed the Prince's health, and in reply the royal visitor offered a few words about the benefits the bridge would bring to the east of Scotland. He then read messages of good wishes from the Queen and the Princess of Wales, and announced that Fowler and Thompson were to be honoured with baronetcies, and Baker and Arrol with knighthoods. These were the first of a host of honours showered on the bridge's creators, not only in this country but abroad, in the following years.

Fowler replied for the engineers, and referred to the opponents of the bridge. "It is very curious to watch the manner of retreat of these prophets of failure when results prove they have been mistaken," he said, "and I could tell you some very curious stories connected with the Forth Bridge. But on this day I feel I can afford to be magnanimous, and I shall say nothing ill-natured about any of them—not even the astronomers."

Poor Sir George Airey; even on this day he did not escape the scorn of the engineers.

It is astonishing how little the design of the Forth Bridge has dated, and how elegantly simple and functional it looks today. Of how many structures can that be said after three-quarters of a century? Yet it was built in an age when architecture was going through Victorian tortures, when simplicity of line was unknown. Of course there were critics who thought it would be beautified by the addition of whorls, and there were others who considered the design just downright ugly. Spokesmen for the latter was William Morris who visited Edinburgh a few months before the bridge was opened and said: "There never will be an architecture in iron, every improvement in machinery being uglier, until we reach the supremest specimen of all ugliness—the Forth Bridge."

As usual Baker was left to answer, and he did so effectively in an address to the Edinburgh Literary Institute:

"Probably Mr. Morris would judge the beauty of a design from the same standpoint whether it was for a bridge a mile long, or for a silver chimney ornament. It is impossible for anyone to pronounce authoritatively on the beauty of an object without knowing its functions. The marble columns of the Parthenon are beautiful where they stand, but if we took one and bored a hole through its axis and used it as a funnel of an Atlantic liner, it would, to my mind, cease to be beautiful, but, of course, Mr. Morris might think otherwise."

Baker said he had often been asked why he did not make his bridge a true arc, and his reply was that to have done so would have been a material falsehood. The Forth Bridge was not an arch, and it said so for itself.

And on ornamentation he said it would have been futile to have embellished the cantilevers. People would search in vain for a moulded capping or cornice—the object had been to arrange the leading lines of the structure so that they conveyed the idea of strength and stability. This, in such a structure, seemed to be at once the truest and the highest art.

In the world of art this opinion was endorsed. Writing to Fowler a few days later Royal Academician Alfred Waterhouse said: "One feature especially delights me—the absence of all ornament. Any architectural detail borrowed from any style would have been out of place in such a work. As it is the bridge is a style unto itself; the simple directness of purpose with which it does its work is splendid, and invests your vast monument with a kind of beauty of its own, differing though it certainly does from all the beautiful things I have ever seen."

Still the critics were not silenced. Lord Rosebery described the bridge as "that monster of utility", and an author writing twenty years after the bridge was opened said: "The curves are not things of beauty, the towering supports between the spans, which might have formed graceful and soaring spires, are cut off bluntly on top at the moment their utilitarian purpose is achieved. Judicious painting even would have rendered the result less bald, the use of gilt here and there might have made it glorious; but no, a coat of red lead suffices to preserve the steel plates from rust."

Benjamin Baker had been dead three years by then, and no answer was made to that attack.

Early in 1889 a group of Edinburgh business men interested in electricity realized that the completion of the Forth Bridge would bring into the capital a large number of sightseers, so they decided to stage an electrical display. Under Mr. Lee Bapty plans were laid for the exhibition, the scope of which grew until the 1890 Exhibition covered a fifty-acre site at Merchiston. In addition to the electrical display there were international exhibits, a collection of historical musical instruments, art galleries, old railway rolling stock, a music hall, and a Japanese village, and while all this attracted thousands of visitors, the real sight at Edinburgh that year was the Forth Bridge.

Art and aesthetics apart, the public admired the Forth Bridge, even if they were at first reluctant to travel over it. The traditional way to Aberdeen had been by the North Western and Caledonian Railways, known as the West Coast route, but the Forth Bridge dramatically altered all that, for it produced a route following the East Coast which was some sixteen miles shorter. The Great Northern, North Eastern and North British which made up the East Coast route had already competed against the West Coast in 1888 to capture the Edinburgh traffic, and in the uneasy truce which existed in 1890 the public realized that it could only be a question of time before war broke out again for supremacy north of Edinburgh.

The Forth Bridge enabled the East Coast lines to cut an hour off their fourteen-hour night journey from King's Cross to Aberdeen, but the competition this might have been expected to bring about did not materialize. The West Coast companies were content to bring their train into Aberdeen behind the rival one, and the five years after the opening of the bridge brought no more than a few skirmishes.

The railway race of 1895, as the competition became known, began in June when the West Coast announced that their 8 p.m. train from Euston would be retimed to arrive in Aberdeen at 7.40 a.m.—only five minutes behind the East Coast one. That set off a series of cuts over the next few weeks as the East Coast replied with a time of 7.20 and the West Coast with 7 a.m., slicing forty minutes off the scheduled time at a stroke.

But these accelerations were on paper only, and bore no relation to the real times of the trains. In fact when the West Coast companies got down to competing in earnest they actually brought their train into Aberdeen on the morning of 17 July at 6.21—thirty-nine minutes ahead of time. This brought more cuts in the time tables—the East Coast train would arrive at 6.45 and the West Coast at 6.40; the East Coast at 6.25 and the West Coast at 6.20. It was now the end of July, and although the companies denied that they were racing, the public and Press knew differently and watched with fascination.

On the first morning when the last of these cuts came into operation the East Coast train made a magnificent effort over much of the journey, but was held up after it crossed the Scottish Border and arrived in Aberdeen only five minutes early, at 6.20, to find that the West Coast train had been in since 6.5.

136

The next morning the West Coast express was even earlier, arriving at 5.59. But there the racing ended for a fortnight while the traffic for the grouse season was too heavy to permit racing.

It was 18 August when the last phase of the race began. The two trains reached Kinnaber Junction simultaneously, and the Caledonian signalman courteously accepted the East Coast train first so that it arrived at Aberdeen at 6.17, ahead of schedule for the first time that month.

Then followed the final cuts in the timetable—forty-five minutes off each route, making the total reduction in the course of seven weeks two and a quarter hours on the West Coast and one hour and fifty-five minutes on the East Coast. Again timetables were ignored, and the West Coast, sending a second train behind its racer to collect those passengers who were either too nervous or too late to join the racing train, reached Aberdeen at 5.15. With four intermediate stops it had covered the 540 miles in 555 minutes. On that night the East Coast companies slipped badly when the North British held the train to the timetable, and it arrived at 5.31—nine minutes early but sixteen minutes behind its opponent.

Next night the King's Cross express was determined to beat the West Coast one, and it must have been galling for its crew to arrive at Kinnaber and find they had been beaten by one minute. That night the Euston train covered the 540 miles in 538 minutes.

On 21 August the East Coast companies once more determined to break the record, and they did. It was 4.40 on the morning of 22 August when their train steamed into Aberdeen, fourteen-and-a-half minutes in front of the Euston express.

But the West Coast had its revenge; by cutting the weight of its train down to the minimum it succeeded in reaching Aberdeen at 4.23, a clear winner.

By common consent the racing ended there. Since June the West Coast had cut the time of the night journey from eleven hours and forty minutes to eight hours and twenty-three minutes. The public got a faster train service as a result of the races if one ignores the discomfort of the racing trains and the inconvenience of being turned out on to a chilly Aberdeen platform in the middle of the night.

However, after the racing an agreement followed fixing reasonable schedules which could be adhered to by trains carrying normal traffic, and the Forth Bridge slowly became popular as the route to Aberdeen.

In fact the Forth Bridge gradually became an accepted part of the scenery of the Forth estuary, and distrust gradually ebbed away, leaving the bridge as the engineering marvel of the Kingdom.

For many years maintenance of the bridge was in the hands of sailors who had served aboard windjammers, and whose ability to scramble among rigging fitted them to climb among the steel "rigging" of the Forth Bridge. But as these men disappeared their places were taken by ordinary workmen with a head for heights and an ability to take extreme care as they work in precarious positions.

Riveters, platelayers, carpenters and painters work all the year round to maintain the bridge and inspect it for faults or deterioration in the metal fabric from action of the river and rainwater, or from the vibration of trains passing over.

The one mile and a thousand yards of track is in the care of eight permanent way men, and there is a team of riggers to set up staging from which the dangerous work is done. However, the job which caught the public imagination from the first, and still holds it, is the painting of the bridge. The job takes three years and as soon as it is finished it is time to start all over again. There are more than twenty painters constantly at work during these three years, and they use fifty tons of paint for the task. A paint brush lasts less than a fortnight.

Painting begins at the topmost point of the bridge, and the painters are slowly lowered as the work proceeds. Their whereabouts at any given time is easy to locate from the brilliant streak of fresh paint on the flank of the bridge, and if that does not pinpoint the men then the safety boat does. When the men are working aloft on the structure this rescue boat, with a crew of two, always hovers below in case of accidents.

Accidents, however, on the Forth Bridge are rare, as the men

138

know that extreme care is required all the time. Perhaps the attitude of the men is best summed up by one who has worked on the bridge for nearly half a century as painter, rigger, foreman, and inspector. "It's a fine healthy life," he says. And he looks as fit as a fiddle on it.

CHAPTER ELEVEN

ROAD OVER THE RIVER

S O M E people flatly refused to trust themselves to the Forth Bridge; they continued to travel by the Queensferry and Granton-Burntisland ferries, glowering at the bridge which they considered an unnecessary temptation to providence. As time passed the bridge remained standing and these diehards died off, leaving the ferries to a few cyclists and an occasional tramp. By Act of Parliament the railway company had to continue to operate the ferries, but it did so on a greatly reduced scale.

On the Granton-Burntisland run it meant farewell to the *Leviathan, John Stirling, Auld Reekie, Thane of Fife, Balbirnie* and *Kinloch*—in fact to all of the gallant North British ships except the *William Muir*, which plied the firth for nearly half a century more with a break of only a couple of years during the First World War when she swept for mines. In 1937 the *William Muir's* place was taken by a new *Thane of Fife* which maintained the service until the ferry was suspended in March, 1940.

The Forth Bridge brought changes to the Queensferry, too. The *John Beaumont*, which was still plying the estuary after being raised and refitted in 1879, was disposed of, and within three years the North British had also handed over the running rights of the ferries to Messrs. David Wilson and Son, a local company from Bo'ness, From the last day of September 1893, until the death of the sole partner in the firm in 1919, Wilsons operated the ferry, and then their successors, Leith

Salvage & Towage Company took it over and continued to run it until November 1926, when the railway—now the London and North Eastern Railway—resumed control.

As in the past when the death knell seemed to be sounding for the Queensferry a miracle brought it new life. The miracle this time was the motor-car. As the numbers of vehicles on the roads grew, and the railways were to a large degree superseded, Fife once more became the isolated and remote place she had been before the railway bridge was built. The Queensferry began to take a few vehicles—the *Dundee*, which ran from 1926, for example, could accommodate three lorries and two cars—but that was quite inadequate. What was needed was another bridge over the Forth, a road bridge which would open up Fife again.

First place to stake its claim was Alloa, which may seem very far upstream, but it had the merit of being bridged comparatively cheaply and of being suitably placed to take traffic from Glasgow and the west as well as from the east. There had been a proposal for a bridge here as long before as 1807, and in the spring of 1919 the idea was revived, as a means of relieving Stirling Bridge. The firm of Mott, Hay & Anderson produced a plan, which interested the Government sufficiently for it to spend £3,000 on a survey. Although this showed that the building of the bridge could be justified, the kind of money needed for the project simply was not available in the early 1920's.

In 1923 a second scheme for bridging the Forth was proposed. James Inglis Kerr was a Fife man, who had long devoted himself to transport and roads. He was editor of a number of publications connected with travel and motoring, including the *SMT Magazine*, the old Scottish Motor Traction Company publication, from which *Scotland's Magazine* has grown.

Inglis Kerr gave much thought to the question of linking Fife with the Lothians, and he summoned the Press to the Hawes Inn, on Friday 2 November 1923, to tell them of his plan. Fife badly needed a road link with the south, he said, and the obvious answer was to adapt the railway bridge to take motor traffic, or to improve the ferries. The bridge-builders had squashed the idea of adding a roadway to the existing bridge, and the improvement of the ferry could be no more than a compromise, so Inglis Kerr proposed a bridge at the Queensferry which, with those already suggested for the Tay and Tweed, would be the last link in the highway from Dover to John o' Groats. Such a bridge would cost £2,500,000 to £3,000,000, but it would give much needed employment to five thousand men for five years, and it would be an economic boon to the community at large.

Details had been shown to the Government quite unofficially, but Inglis Kerr had in his pocket a letter from Sir Henry Maybury, of the Ministry of Transport, saying, "I agree absolutely that if such a scheme could be carried out it would be an immense advantage to the road and bridge communications of the country. You will realize I have no authority to pledge the Minister to any action therein, but you may count upon whatever personal assistance I can give in your missionary efforts to enthuse interest in a scheme having so much promise for the future."

The bridge was to be a suspension one, carrying a 40-foot road and two nine-foot paths. The central pier would be on Inchgarvie beside the railway bridge, although the two bridges would not be parallel. While the northern ends of both would be close together at North Queensferry, the road bridge would begin on the south side at a point on the Edinburgh–South Queensferry road near the top of the Hawes Brae.

The seeds sown at the Hawes Inn that day germinated early the following year, when a meeting was called at the Caledonian Hotel, Edinburgh. The Ministry of Transport had three representatives present as Inglis Kerr repeated his plan to delegates from Edinburgh, Linlithgow, Dunfermline, South Queensferry, North Queensferry, Inverkeithing, Perth, Kirkcaldy and Dundee, and to representatives from the motoring organizations. Inglis Kerr showed maps and plans of his bridge, and Sir Henry Maybury told delegates that there were no engineering difficulties to prevent it from being built. Sir Henry took the opportunity of airing the subject again a little afterwards when he spoke at a luncheon at the City Chambers in Edinburgh, to mark the beginning of the Edinburgh section of the Edinburgh–Glasgow road.

The bridge project was now well and truly launched, and Inglis Kerr went to London on 28 March 1924 to address a meeting in a committee-room at the House of Commons. There were thirty Scottish Members of Parliament present, and this meeting resulted in the formation of a committee to urge the scheme on the Ministry of Transport and to try to persuade the Government at least to have a survey made.

The Minister of Transport in the Labour Government, Mr. Harry Gosling, agreed on 25 April to pay three-quarters of the £10,000 which it was estimated that such a survey would cost. Who was to pay the other quarter? The rest of the year was taken up with negotiations between various councils in Scotland, for, although all were willing to say that a bridge was necessary, few were prepared to pay for it.

Despite the defeat of the Labour Government in October 1924, the offer from the Ministry of Transport still held good, and a conference of local authorities concerned was eventually convened in Edinburgh, on Wednesday, 21 January 1925. At this delegates were actually shown a preliminary survey and plans for a suspension bridge costing £4,000,000 which would form an integral part of the road system of Eastern Scotland.

Such a figure terrified the delegates. If they contributed to the survey they might be deemed to be agreeing also to pay a proportion of the building cost, and who knew whether it might not exceed the £4,000,000 estimate.

There was therefore plenty of support for the Earl of Elgin's motion that the state should pay the whole of the survey bill, and it took a further six months of hard negotiations to break the resistance of the Scottish local authorities sufficiently for them to agree to contribute £1,500.

On that basis Mott, Hay & Anderson were commissioned to survey the estuary at Queensferry, a job which took them until the autumn of 1928. Their findings, presented to the Ministry and local authorities in the following July, dealt with three sites—at Beamer Rock, near Rosyth; a spot downstream from the railway bridge; and at Dalmeny, a mile or so nearer Edinburgh. The engineers rejected the first site because it was so near the dredged channel leading to Rosyth that the Admiralty would almost certainly object, and the second was turned down on the grounds that the railway company would oppose it and in any case it would spoil the appearance of the railway bridge. That left Dalmeny, where they estimated that a suspension bridge could be erected for £6,000,000.

Lord Elgin, Fife County Council's Convener and its loudest voice in opposition to the bridge, hardly gave the ink of the report time to dry before he was asking who was to pay such an immense sum, and who was to maintain the bridge once it was built. It was the beginning of a long campaign by Lord Elgin against the bridge, and it was the type of question which, though pertinent enough, was to delay the building by more years than anyone today cares to admit to.

By this time Labour was in power once more and anxious to show its progressiveness to all. The Government was therefore well disposed towards the project, and all that was needed at that moment was for the local authorities to come a little way towards meeting the cost for a substantial grant to be forthcoming from the Road Fund. But this the local authorities were unwilling to do. In fact, Lord Elgin, in moving that Fife County Council should send representatives to a meeting called in Edinburgh on 9 October, put forward an alternative scheme for an express ferry service, which would take only £370,000 —a sixteenth of the cost of the bridge.

With that view prevailing across the estuary the Edinburgh Conference could hardly be expected to succeed. Delegates were agreed on one thing—the bridge would be a vital link in a national highway system, with all of the emphasis on the word "national". It should therefore be deemed a national project, with not one halfpenny of the cost borne locally. Furthermore, the approaches to the bridge should be included in the cost so that in effect the local authorities would pay nothing towards the great amenity which they wanted.

Copies of these resolutions were sent to the Prime Minister, to the Secretary of State for Scotland, and to the Minister of

Transport, who was also asked to receive a deputation. Herbert Morrison was now in charge of the Ministry, and he was quick to point out that the construction of roads and bridges was not a national matter, but was for the highways authorities concerned, with such assistance as might be available from the Road Fund. While he was prepared to receive a deputation he thought the Scottish councils ought to reconsider the amount of their responsibility before a deputation came south.

In reply Edinburgh Town Clerk averred that the Government had previously regarded the scheme as a national one, and even if the authorities were willing to contribute an equitable basis could not be worked out. The Minister had undertaken to find out whether the project was feasible, and he should now complete the job by carrying out the inquiry into economic justification.

In fact, if Morrison adhered to his attitude it was tantamount to saying that the project was turned down as there was little chance of the local authorities promoting so great a scheme. The Minister was again asked to receive a deputation, and this time he agreed.

On 8 January 1930, Morrison met the Scottish representatives; the Lord Provost, as spokesman, claimed that the bridge would mainly benefit through traffic and so should be a national project. However, there was one spark of hope—both Edinburgh and Dunfermline were now prepared to make a limited contribution.

As the Lord Provost opened this door, Lord Elgin slammed it again. Speaking on behalf of Fife County Council and the Forth Conservancy Board he said that both of these bodies doubted whether the expenditure on a bridge was justified, and he suggested that the answer might be to improve the ferries and build a bridge further up the river.

Morrison again refused to pay for the bridge out of the Road Fund, and urged the deputation to study the economic justification again. In fact he agreed with Lord Elgin that they should think in terms of an improved ferry in association with the Alloa bridge, for which plans existed and building of which could be started quickly.

Lord Elgin had not been thinking of Alloa when he suggested a bridge further up the Forth—he had in mind Kincardine-on-Forth, which was reckoned to be the lowest point at which the upper estuary could be bridged economically. Lord Elgin now gave all his support to Kincardine.

Not everyone agreed, and perhaps the wisest words were spoken by Edinburgh City Treasurer when he pleaded with the Minister to take the initiative. "To expect agreement among local authorities, each one looking at the question from a selfish viewpoint and not from a national viewpoint, is nothing short of fatuous optimism," he said.

A conference of local authorities proved the Treasurer's point. Lord Provost Whitson of Edinburgh said his city was willing to contribute £100,000 and that others should offer something also to show that they were in earnest, but Lord Elgin again opposed him. Finally Elgin agreed that a committee should be appointed to confer on the bridge question, but in return he insisted that they should support his Kincardine scheme.

Lord Elgin had to face minor defeats however. When his Kincardine scheme was brought before Dunfermline District Committee he was told he was like a jack in the box—jumping up to destroy every other scheme as it came near to fruition, and the committee turned his scheme down by twelve votes to nine.

Nevertheless Sir Alexander Gibb & Partners were asked to report on the possibility of bridging the Forth at Kincardine, and in this they were helped by borings which the Caledonian Railway had made at the site in 1890. These showed that although rock lay a few feet below the riverbed on the northern side of the river, there was a deep fault on the south side where the rock dipped away, making it difficult to found piers. On this southern section, where forty or fifty feet of mud had been deposited on a bed of gravel, the engineers suggested that groups of reinforced concrete piles 65 to 70 feet long might be driven through the mud into the gravel, and on these the concrete piers could be constructed.

By June 1930 the merits of the Alloa and Kincardine schemes

had been assessed, and were set before a conference at Stirling. Labour was in power and was willing to give either of the bridges its blessing, so now Lord Ponsonby, of the Ministry of Transport, took the chair at a meeting of delegates representing the Forth Conservancy Board and the burghs of Alloa, Dunfermline, Falkirk and Stirling.

From the start Lord Ponsonby made it clear that they were there to discuss a bridge over the upper Forth and not one in opposition to Queensferry. The Government considered that traffic warranted this second bridge, and had asked for reports on comparable structures at Alloa and Kincardine. On the basis of a 30-foot carriageway, with footpaths on either side, and a 100-foot swing opening to let shipping pass through, the cost at Alloa would be £418,000 compared with £385,000 at Kincardine.

Kincardine won on price, and it also had the advantage of being the lowest point at which the Forth could be bridged economically and yet reasonably convenient to the east as well as the west. Thus the decision went in favour of Kincardine. The three counties involved—Stirling, Clackmannan, and Fife —were quick to push ahead with the bridge once the decision had been taken, and in 1931 a Provisional Order was approved, with the Ministry of Transport agreeing to pay 85 per cent of the bill for both bridge and road works associated with it. Towards the end of the year the work was put out to tender.

Then came a blow—economic crisis and the consequent investigation into projects in hand brought attacks on the grandiose bridge schemes being financed by the Road Fund, and consequently brought the Kincardine preparations to a halt. It took two years of badgering and lobbying to get them under way again, and then only with a 10 per cent cut in the Government's contribution.

The tender of the Cleveland Bridge & Engineering Company was accepted for the main works, foundations, and superstructure, including roadways and footpaths, and on Wednesday, 20 December 1933, Lord Bruce, eldest son of Lord Elgin, cut the first turf to institute the works.

At Kincardine the shore-to-shore width is 2,400 feet, but the actual length of the bridge was to be nearly 300 feet more, making it the longest road bridge in Britain at the time. On either side of the central opening there were seven steel spans of 100 feet each, and the bridge was completed by a series of smaller shoreward spans, three on the south side and nine on the north.

As a start a bypass road was built through Kincardine, and thirty houses were put up on the south bank of the river to accommodate people whose homes had to be demolished to make way for the road. This northern approach road was opened by the Countess of Mar and Kellie in 1934.

Two years later the bridge was ready, and it was opened on 29 October 1936. Stirling, Clackmannan and Fife shared the honours. After a series of speeches by representatives of the Ministry of Transport, the engineers and contractors, the conveners of the three counties, C. E. Horsburgh, the Earl of Mar and Kellie, and the Earl of Elgin each pressed a switch to close the swing span so that the official party could cross the bridge in a procession headed by Dunfermline Pipe Band.

The guests then inspected the mechanism for operating the swing span, and watched it open the span again so that the Forth Conservancy Board's vessel, *Corega*, could pass through. The bridge was closed again and the official party adjourned to a marquee where light refreshments awaited them. Light refreshments! Changed days from the splendid luncheon when the railway bridge at Queensferry was opened in 1890.

At three o'clock the bridge was opened to the public.

The second part of Lord Elgin's plan was for an improved ferry service, and here the Dumbarton shipbuilding firm of William Denny & Brothers brought forward an idea. These were difficult times for shipbuilding, with empty order books and many men unemployed, so Sir Maurice Denny approached the L.N.E.R. and suggested that in view of the additional traffic on the roads they should build two new ferries.

The railway company was not keen, but countered with another suggestion—why did Denny's not build the two ferries themselves and take over the operation of the ferry? Denny

Brothers accepted, and signed a ten-year agreement to manage the ferry.

On 1 March 1934, they took over the Queensferry with their first ship, a 149-foot long diesel-electric paddle-driven ship, the *Queen Margaret*, which was joined a few weeks later by a second, the *Robert the Bruce*. Both of these were double-ended to save delays by having to turn round at the end of each trip. Thus the two ferries were able to maintain a half-hourly service with a carrying capacity of twenty-eight motor-cars and 500 passengers on each trip. In a single month during that first summer the *Queen Margaret* and *Robert the Bruce* carried nearly 12,000 vehicles and 44,000 passengers.

Paradoxically the success of the new ferries was the principal reason for their failure, for the excellent service attracted more cars which in turn led to inadequate capacity and queues at peak periods. By the late 1930's it was clear that a third ferry was needed to cope with the tourist rush in summer and allow for winter overhauls. However, the Second World War made the supply of this ship impossible until 1949, when the *Mary Queen of Scots* joined the Forth fleet.

Still the traffic continued to increase, and the queues at the ferry became a monotonously repeated complaint from both tourist and business traveller alike. It was reaching the stage where it would be quicker to make the long detour by Kincardine rather than wait in an impatient line at Queensferry. In fact, the Antiquary would have been at home at Queensferry, except that he could not dismount and enjoy the hospitality of the Hawes Inn until a ferry was available. A fourth ship, the *Sir William Wallace* was added to the Queensferry fleet in March 1956, enabling Denny Brothers to run a fifteen-minute service through most of the year, and a twenty-minute one in the four winter months. These four ships made some 40,000 crossings a year carrying 1,250,000 passengers, 600,000 cars and 200,000 commercial vehicles. But for the building of the Forth Road Bridge today a fifth vessel would be needed already.

CHAPTER TWELVE

THE SITE IS CHOSEN . . .

EDINBURGH was not at all pleased when the Earl of Elgin carried his scheme for the Kincardine Bridge, and the promise of improved services at Queensferry did little to quell anger in the capital. Inglis Kerr had said at the very beginning that new ferries could be no more than a stopgap, and that the bridge on the upper Forth could never bring Midlothian closer to the industrial area of the Fife coalfield.

In February 1931, a new body appeared as sponsors of a report on Forth crossings generally. This Joint Committee of Inquiry represented many important business interests in Edinburgh and Leith, among them the Chambers of Commerce, the Merchant Company, Rotary Club, City Business Club, and Leith Dock Commission. This report emphasised that a road bridge over the lower Forth was the ultimate solution, and the committee worked towards that goal throughout the difficult early 1930's when money was short and the little that was available was being directed towards Kincardine.

About this time Mott, Hay & Anderson began to look for alternative sites to the three which had been considered previously, and to which there had been so much opposition. At the end of July 1931, they came up with one—where the Mackintosh Rock ruffled the surface of the river upstream from the railway bridge. A bridge here with a single span of 3,000 feet could strike out from the shore just west of South Queensferry to join the Dunfermline road a little after it left the Inverkeithing road. In fact this is where the bridge was eventually to be built. For a structure carrying a 50-foot roadway the cost would be £4,250,000, and for a 40-foot one it would be £3,800,000.

Again Lord Elgin displayed the jack-in-the-box propensities of which he had been accused already by suggesting yet another site—from Hopetoun to Rosyth. He fought so forcefully for this that the Ministry of Transport was persuaded to promise three-quarters of the cost of surveying this site, but when the economic crisis came he was unable to stop the Ministry from calling off the survey.

The Joint Committee, angered at the delay and at being snubbed by the Secretary of State for Scotland who refused to receive its members, decided to issue a report to the public in 1933. As the year progressed and the Kincardine scheme was taken up again and actually put in hand, the committee—now strengthened by the support of the Automobile Association and the Royal Scottish Automobile Club—again issued its report with a supplement.

"A bridge at Kincardine, while of local value, cannot serve the large volume of present and potential road traffic," said the report, adding that it would facilitate vehicles travelling from the west only. The new ferries, which were now nearing completion at Denny's would not be able to cope with the traffic either, so if the bridge did not come within the scope of the Road Fund, the Government should take into account the saving in dole payments which its construction would bring, and it might even consider raising part of the money by tolls.

In the two years between the reports of the Joint Committee the demand for the road bridge had become more strident, with many Scottish M.P.s cajoling an unwilling Government to act. In July 1934, the work of these various pressure groups was co-ordinated to form the Forth Bridge Promotion Committee, which was basically the old joint committee backed by a number of other organizations and individuals. Under the direction of Sir Alexander Stevenson and Major Macdonald Smith this committee called meetings throughout Fife and the Lothians to push, plead, and prod for action.

When Mr. L. Hore-Belisha, the Minister of Transport, announced a five-year plan for the roads in a speech at Birmingham on Saturday, 26 January 1935, a telegram went off to him immediately, saying: "Forth Road Bridge Promotion Committee deeply interested in Minister's five-year plan, and sincerely hope Queensferry road bridge is included in it."

It was not, but the committee continued its work by launching a propaganda campaign in West Lothian the following month.

Occasionally the publicity backfired, as at Bo'ness on the night when the West Lothian campaign was opened. Those who attended were handed leaflets in support of a scheme to dam the river and run a road from the Lothians to Fife along the top of the barrage. The project would give employment to the thousands of workless in Central Scotland, and when completed it would provide a huge supply of electricity and enable the east to set up a ship-building industry as great as that of the Clyde.

"Businessmen on the Forth have been for long content to play second fiddle to the Clyde in the matter of ship-building," stated the dam manifesto. "With the dam completed and creating a huge deep-water lake there would be no need to work out fine calculations for the launching of any size of ship."

In 1934, largely due to the Lord Provost of Edinburgh, Sir William Thomson, the Mackintosh Rock site survey was completed, and in the following year he gave the project another push by persuading Edinburgh Town Council to accept this as the best site, and by calling a conference of neighbouring local authorities in March 1935.

Sir William was under no illusion as to the prospect of having the bridge built by the state, and when a mass meeting was held at the Usher Hall just before the Edinburgh Conference, he suggested that if the Ministry of Transport would pay three-quarters of the bill then the local authorities ought to agree to find the rest. As the largest council, Edinburgh should offer half of the local authorities' share—a sportsmanlike thing to do, said Sir William—and some of the money found locally could be recovered from tolls and rates.

Although the mass meeting declared unanimously in favour of the bridge all of the delegates were by no means prepared to accept the scheme. Again trouble came from Fife and Lord Elgin, who opposed the Mackintosh Rock site "until its feasibility had been proved", insisted on completion of the Hopetoun-Rosyth survey plus similar ones at the Mackintosh Rock and possibly the Beamer Rock as well. Eventually the conference adjourned so that Fife County Council could again consider the Mackintosh Rock site which the others favoured.

Completion of the Mackintosh Rock survey in June 1935 showed that the borings were successful, and that "satisfactory foundation can be obtained at a lesser depth than we had allowed for in our estimate of the cost". In fact the saving was in the region of £750,000.

The survey of the Hopetoun-Rosyth site was in the hands of Sir Alexander Gibb and Partners who produced an interim report in October 1935 in which they commented that they were "reluctant to suggest the expenditure of further money in driving the test piles". Lord Elgin saw defeat and issued a statement in reply to "the many and varied misrepresentations of Fife's position, given in public speeches". Fife's guiding principle, he said, had always been the best bridge, at the best site, at the best price. A month later he told the Press that, although it had been continuously cast in the teeth of Fife County Council that they had obstructed the building of the bridge, it was Fife that had got the project out of cold storage in which the 1931 economic crisis had placed it.

In mid-October another conference was called in Edinburgh and a deputation was appointed to travel south to find out just how much the Government would be prepared to spend on the road bridge. But before this meeting could be arranged Fife County Council at last agreed to support the Mackintosh Rock plan. All that remained was to pin the Ministry down to naming a figure.

Towards the end of February 1936 there came another blow, when Hore-Belisha announced that he could not see his way, on the basis of the traffic figures before him, to offer any grant at all.

153

The local authorities' Forth Road Bridge Joint Committee at once set about proving the Minister wrong. Quickly a survey of traffic was organized in a small area around the ferry, and this showed that three-quarters of a million vehicles could be expected to use a bridge at Queensferry each year. The report of this survey listed twenty-one advantages for bridging the lower Forth, ranging from the claim, which no one disputed, that it would facilitate traffic movement to the relief of unemployment and the saving in expenditure on imported petrol.

Adam Smith was quoted in support of the bridge and its effect in linking up the highways of eastern Scotland. "Good roads . . . by diminishing the expense of carriage put the remote parts of the country more surely upon a level with those in the neighbourhood of the town," he had written. "They are, upon that account, the greatest of all improvements."

And even more important were the comments of prospective users. Typical of these were: "The bridge would open up new markets", and "At present I am unable, owing to the long distance by road, to estimate for or execute any work on the other side of the Forth".

And even south of the Border notice was being taken of the need for a road across the lower Forth. In July 1936, the *Observer* published a leader entitled "Roads and Vision". This said: "We have a road called the Great North Road. At no point is it great. For only 220 miles is it north. At Scotch Corner it turns aside from Scotland and meanders north-west, due west, through Carlisle, and then north-east, a narrow tram-ridden road, seared with level crossings, hampered by mining villages, until it reaches Scotland's capital at last. The north road from Edinburgh is even worse. There are no road bridges over the Forth or Tay. Nor, for the matter of that, are there road bridges spanning essential points of Humber and Severn. In fact, in sad fact, call them what we will, Britain has no "Great" roads. A real Great North Road would start at Dover, and run north to Scotch Corner, and due north again across the rivers, and never draw breath till it reached John o' Groats. That would be something like a road. Something, indeed, almost like a Roman road."

The road bridge was not a party issue, and both a Labour and a Unionist Member put down a question in the Commons in November 1936 asking the Minister of Transport if he was in a position to make a statement on Government policy regarding the Forth Road Bridge. Hore-Belisha, in a written answer, took the opportunity to write off not only the Forth Bridge, but the Humber and Severn ones as well. "His Majesty's Government have come to the conclusion that they would not be justified in embarking upon the execution of these public works at the present moment, but this decision does not exclude the reconsideration of these projects at a later date," he said.

Sir William Thomson, who had done so much to unify the local authorities during his term of office as Lord Provost of Edinburgh, protested that a few millions spread over six or seven years could not ruin the country, and the Promotion Committee should keep up its pressure. But the protests were half-hearted, for it was at last becoming apparent that Europe was hastening towards war, and an enormous defence programme had to be embarked on urgently. At a meeting of the local authorities in Edinburgh, Lord Provost Louis S. Gumley admitted that he had no alternative but to accept that defence justified the delay.

That was virtually the end of the Forth Road Bridge project for a decade; as the war neared the scheme was pushed into the background and less and less was heard of it. While the ferry delays annoyed travellers they accepted them as inevitable. In Scottish hearts the hope still lay that, come better times, the bridge might yet be built.

And as hope for the bridge died in the autumn of 1936 so also did the man who had begun it all. James Inglis Kerr, the man who had called the first Press conference in 1923, died on 11 September. In thirteen years he had seen the cause grow, suffer setback after setback, and yet come ever nearer to fruition. He had seen dissenting authorities come round to accepting a site, and he had watched the scheme reach the stage where it was apparent that, although the threat of war might postpone the project, it could not kill it altogether.

CHAPTER THIRTEEN

. . . AND CHOSEN AGAIN

ALTHOUGH the war was not yet over, thoughts began to turn by 1943 to post-war reconstruction and roads fit to handle the surge of traffic which peace would bring. The word motorway entered the language and, not unnaturally,, hopes rose that a motorway might sweep majestically across the Forth.

At this time Edinburgh had one of her most colourful and dynamic Lord Provosts, Will Y. Darling, who was of course also chairman of the local authorities' Road Bridge Joint Committee. Undoubtedly there would be many conflicting projects clamouring for cash, and the road bridge sponsors wanted to be certain that their scheme would be one of the winning ones. Accordingly a conference of local authorities was called in Edinburgh at the beginning of the year, and at this it was unanimously decided to push ahead with the plans which could be set before the Ministry of War Transport.

So far as anyone knew the 1935 agreement on the Mackintosh Rock site still held good, but now Lord Elgin returned to the fray with yet another plan. This time it was for a bridge sharing Inchgarvie with the railway one, and only 400 feet away from it at the closest point. Two strides of 2,400 feet would take the bridge over the estuary, and at the northern end a further bridge would be needed to cross Inverkeithing Bay.

Elgin put his scheme before the committee on Tuesday 22 December 1943, by which time he had shown the plans to the Admiralty and strengthened his case by obtaining a reply that the Lords of the Admiralty saw no objection to it. On the other hand they had seen no objection to the Mackintosh Rock site in 1935 either.

More pertinent to the mind of Treasurer Andrew Murray of Edinburgh was the resemblance which the Elgin plan bore to that which Mott, Hay & Anderson had rejected in 1930 and to an even earlier one by Inglis Kerr. Elgin argued that his bridge used Inchgarvie and was much shorter than the 1930 one, although it was "not dissimilar" to that proposed by Inglis Kerr.

The great merits of the new project, he claimed, were that it would give better access roads—slicing through Inverkeithing to do so, it should be pointed out—and that it would constitute no hazard to navigation. Furthermore, the scheme would not be opposed by the Forth Conservancy Board, while that at the Mackintosh Rock would be. Elgin still carried much weight, and the committee agreed "without departing from the Mackintosh Rock site" to submit his plan to their engineers.

The engineers rejected the Inchgarvie bridge, and so also did the joint committee after Will Y. Darling had told them that if the Admiralty supported the Elgin plan the Royal Air Force would oppose it because they considered that two huge bridges side by side would make too good a target for enemy bombers. Darling did not take the Navy or R.A.F. views too seriously, however, and told the committee: "Do not let us be carried away by these human red herrings. Let us take the best evidence we can get. By and large there is a great measure of agreement that the Mackintosh Rock site is the better site, and if we can be agreed on that unanimously I think we should go forward with it."

Elgin was not defeated yet. He soon had the support of Sir Murdoch Macdonald who had proposed to add a roadway to the rail bridge and then abandoned the idea in favour of Lord Elgin's bridge, and on the initiative of George Mather and a few other M.P.s a private conference was called at the House of Commons on Tuesday 2 May, to give Members details of the Inchgarvie plan.

Darling was not pleased, and in a speech that week-end he

said: "Local authorities may be inclined to wonder if the will of the people in such matters shall prevail."

As a counterblast the local authorities invited every Scottish M.P. to luncheon at Edinburgh City Chambers and then to meet and discuss the road bridge. The meeting took place on Monday, 25 July, and far from rousing enthusiasm it brought a sharp clash which did the cause of the bridge-promoters no good. In the first place, of Scotland's seventy-four M.P.s exactly half sent refusals to join the party; another twenty did not reply at all, and only fourteen turned up on the day.

Will Y. Darling was in the chair and, like a minister who issues rebukes from the pulpit to non-attenders at the kirk on Sunday, he began by telling the fourteen who had taken the trouble to come that he thought M.Ps' interest in the bridge had been "very slight and tepid". Members had not given the local authorities the support they ought to have done, otherwise Elgin's plan would have been scotched and the bridge would have been much further advanced.

This rebuke was more than William Watson, the Member for Dunfermline Burghs could stand. "We have not been consulted in any way by the local authorities, but we are presented by the local authorities with our instructions. So far as I am concerned I resent the lecture that has been delivered to us from the chair."

Neil Maclean, M.P. for Govan, mediated and Sir Will admitted that he had perhaps expressed himself a little strongly. Despite the apologies and subsequent amicable talk it was not a successful exercise in public relations for the committee.

There had been suggestions that the Government should mediate in the war over the site, but Philip Noel Baker, Secretary to the Ministry of War Transport, made it clear in the Commons that he had no intention of doing so.

"I beg Mr. Noel Baker to beware lest he departs unhonoured and unsung from a field where, at any rate, he can make a decision if he cannot make a bridge", commented Sir Will. Mr. Noel Baker would make neither decision nor bridge, much to the annoyance of those who were endeavouring to plan for the post-war period.

Sir Will Darling was eminently quotable on the subject of the bridge, and among the truest pronouncements he made was that this was "a case of how the public were going to make their will effective upon Parliament".

The end of the war brought a new spirit of nationalism everywhere, and Scotland was no exception. The new outlook resulted in the bridge being adopted by every Scot—man, woman and child—as a personal challenge willingly taken up everywhere, and if any bridge deserves the title the people's bridge it is the one which swings gracefully from Lothian to Fife. Even today there are critics in the south who consider the ultimate building of the bridge no more than a sop to Scottish over-sensitivity, just as there are Scots who feel that an English plot delayed the work for a quarter of a century. Perhaps there is a grain of truth in both views.

Arthur Woodburn, M.P. for Clackmannan and East Stirlingshire, asked just as the war was nearing its end about the priority of the bridge in the post-war programme, but was informed that it would not be high on the list. A month later he aired the question in the Commons again, when he told Members that Scotland would build the bridge herself if necessary.

"Two people have approached me spontaneously," he said, "and suggested that they would provide money to start a national fund for the building of the bridge if the Chancellor is prepared to allow Scotland to use its savings for this constructive purpose instead of using them for the general national purposes. The money can be raised in Scotland if that is the only way to build the bridge."

On the same day the Earl of Rosebery gave notice in the House of Lords that he proposed to initiate a debate on post-war reconstruction with particular reference to Prestwick and the Forth Road Bridge. This debate took place on Wednesday, 28 March, when Lord Rosebery expressed the same feeling as Arthur Woodburn had shown. "Let me say at once that there is no question of people in Scotland coming as mendicants to the Government," said Lord Rosebery. "I understand from financial experts that we in Scotland could perfectly well finance the bridge ourselves, as long, of course, as we got a grant from the Road Fund, and that grant is our due."

In reply Lord Leathers, Minister of War Transport, said he was not impressed with the economic justification of the bridge in the face of the £40,000,000 arrears in road repairs which had accumulated during the war. While admitting some right on the Government side the *Glasgow Herald* chided Leathers for failing to give any indication that he realized the wider aspects of the problem. "He might almost have been dealing with a project for a bridge between Great and Little Pudlington which was of no importance beyond the two hamlets in an obscure county occasionally visited by tourists but ignored by business men," said the *Herald* leading article the following morning.

Although the Scottish peers were determined to embarrass the Government on the bridge question they were not prepared to divide the House; but their debate did have one odd result— it brought about a private meeting of parties interested in the project, and at this a committee was set up to try to obtain a Provisional Order. When this committee met Lord Leathers he promised to approach the Treasury about a grant.

The Minister succeeded in securing a promise of three-quarters of the cost of obtaining a Provisional Order, and when this was announced on the last day of July, Lord Provost John I. Falconer of Edinburgh described it as the biggest step forward in many years.

It was a year later that the Provisional Order was passed, and in the interval peace was made with the railway company which stood to lose a great deal when the road bridge opened. The L.N.E.R. was to receive £15,000 a year for ten years as compensation, and in addition Burntisland Council agreed not to oppose the railway company's application to abandon the Granton–Burntisland ferry.

The sole objectors to the road bridge scheme were the Forth Conservancy Board, and the hearing of their objections took place in July 1946. Lord Clyde, who represented the promoters of the scheme, said that 83 per cent of the population of Scotland lived within two hours' driving distance of the area served by the bridge, and the main coalfields of the future would be in Fife. "We ask you to lift the iron curtain which rests over the Firth of Forth and to approve of a scheme which we are confident we can justify as economically sound, and as the solution of an urgent and crying need," he said.

The Conservancy Board—"one small voice crying in the wilderness", was Lord Clyde's description—claimed that the bridge would injure their rights, and they made much of the hazard to navigation which the bridge would be. They further claimed that the Beamer Rock should be taken away, but this the promoters resisted successfully on the grounds of excessive cost. Within three-and-a-half days the hearing was over and the preamble of the Provisional Order had been proved.

This Provisional Order set up the Forth Road Bridge Joint Board to build the bridge, which, with its approach roads, was now estimated to cost £6,200,000. Parliamentary powers were obtained the following year, but cuts in capital expenditure by the Government held up progress, and it was November 1948 before the next step forward was taken. At last the Ministry of Transport made a grant of £250,000 towards the preliminary costs of the bridge, and agreed that it might now be brought to the contract letting stage, but only on the understanding that work would not begin for a number of years as there were still too many more urgent projects in hand.

It was like a film in slow motion, and Scottish patience ran out as month succeeded month and there was no news of progress. In fact in 1950 the scheme regressed when Sir Bruce White revived the plan for a road to be added to the existing rail bridge, and it took until 1954 to rule that out completely. No sooner had the White scheme been disposed of than another was brought forward—for an underwater "tube" on the bed of the estuary.

Forth tunnels were nothing new of course—the first had been suggested at the beginning of the nineteenth century, and the last one had been reported-on unfavourably in 1938.

This 1955 plan was different, however; it was for a massive reinforced subway, 3,800 feet long, supported on piles so that it lay on the bed of the river or just above it. The site was about

300 yards west of the railway bridge, and the subway would be built in six sections, the largest 700 feet long, each prefabricated at the factory and towed out into the estuary and lowered into place. The segments were to consist of reinforced concrete tubes, in cross section resembling a flattened ellipse, 84 feet wide and 26 feet deep. The interior of the tubes would be divided into four sections, two larger ones forming roadways 22 feet wide and two small ones for ventilation ducts.

A three-man board was appointed to report on the "tube", with Sir William Halcrow as its chairman. This committee met forty times to consider the "tube" and compare it with the bridge. As the panel debated, the subway designer, Mr. G. A. Maunsell, improved on his scheme by suggesting in the late summer of 1955 a new method of assembling the units of the tunnel under water, and then by having a model made to show how the "tube" would be built. Revised estimates put the cost at £5,991,000, and construction time at three years.

Maunsell then submitted his plans for ventilation, and approach roads which the panel compared with those for the bridge, and then referred to local experts. Finally the panel members went over the ground on both sides of the Forth.

Although subways of this type had been built before, and in fact one was under construction at Rotterdam at the time, nothing had been done on the scale needed for the Forth, or under similar conditions. Thus, when they reported in July 1956 the panel wrote: "Quite apart from its scale, however, the scheme submitted presents a number of novel features to which there is little if any background of experience, and which, therefore, fall into the category of imponderables. This does not by any means imply that they are necessarily undesirable or impracticable, but it means that very careful thought must be given to them to ensure that all their implications have been taken into account."

And when the "implications" had been considered the experts felt unable to support the tunnel. The first reason was the danger of a ship sinking on top of it or running into it it in the shallows near the shore, so that the tunnel might be breached and flooded. Maunsell answered that by proposing half-tide banks of quarry refuse for protection, but these would have added a further £150,000 to the cost.

The main criticism of the "tube" scheme however, was that its southern approaches were inadequate, really catering only for traffic from Edinburgh and Leith, and to bring the southern approaches up to the standard to cope with motorway age traffic would add a tremendous amount to the cost.

The subway would also restrict the waterway by as much as a quarter and its maintenance costs would be much higher than those of the bridge.

"In all the circumstances, Halcrow's committee reported, "the bridge scheme appears to offer a more satisfactory solution than the subway to the particular problems presented by the site, and, in the opinion of the panel, is to be preferred on the grounds of economy, suitability and greater freedom from hazard both during construction and when in use."

The Government accepted the report and the road bridge was restored to official favour at a meeting in Edinburgh in June 1956 between the Joint Board and the Secretary of State for Scotland.

Could it be possible that the scheme had cleared the last major hurdle? To Scotsmen who had watched the battle for more than thirty years it hardly seemed likely.

CHAPTER FOURTEEN

SPINNING THE WEB

THE bridge which won victory carried the third longest suspension span in the world—its 3,300 feet surpassed by the Golden Gate Bridge, San Francisco, and the George Washington Bridge, New York. Soon it was to take fourth place, for the Mackinack Bridge, then building in the United States, was to soar across 3,800 feet. However, at least the Forth Road Bridge was to be the longest span in Europe.

The total distance to be bridged was 6,000 feet, with a central span of 3,300 feet and two side ones each 1,337 feet long. There were to be two roads of 24 feet width, plus footpaths and cycle tracks, all carried 150 feet above the river. The great 512-foot towers, which would carry the suspension cables, were to be sited in about 40 feet of water on the Mackintosh Rock and 1,400 feet out from the south bank. It was to be located about half a mile upstream from the railway bridge on the northern shore, and three-quarters of a mile from it on the southern one.

From the £2,500,000 which was the original estimate of bridging the estuary the cost had risen to £6,000,000 at the end of the war, and now it was £14,000,000, with the likelihood of further increases before the bridge was finished. The Government was to contribute £4,650,000 and the local authorities £500,000; the remainder was to be lent by the Treasury and repaid from tolls.

The Government undertook to allow building to start by the end of March 1959, but it improved on that when the Secretary

164

of State told the Commons in January 1957 that the date was to be advanced by eight months. "In short," said the Secretary of State, Mr. John Maclay, "this is the green light to carry on with the scheme."

It was the most welcome cliché Scotland had heard for a very long time.

Almost everybody was happy about this news, and was prepared to offer a comment on it.

"We have now reached a point where it looks as if we have come to the end of an auld sang," said Arthur Woodburn. The Lord Provost of Edinburgh thought it a step in the right direction, and the motoring organizations welcomed the announcement with reservations on tolls, but Nigel Tranter, Convener of the National Forth Road Bridge Promotion Committee, which had been formed a few years earlier to rouse public opinion and prod the Government, said the Government was not being very generous or helpful in advancing the date by a mere eight months.

The designers of the bridge were Mott, Hay & Anderson in association with Freeman, Fox & Partners, and oddly there was a link between these consulting engineers and the builders of the railway bridge. Sir David Anderson, who had played an important part in designing the bridge was a Scot who had gone from St. Andrew's University to work for Sir William Arrol & Company in Glasgow and then to London to join Sir Benjamin Baker, who had played so important a part in designing the railway bridge. After much work in the south, Anderson formed a partnership with Sir Basil Mott and David Hay in the year the plan to bridge the Forth was mooted by Inglis Kerr. David Anderson dearly wanted to see the estuary spanned, and before he died in 1933 he had designed the bridge which was to cross it.

Another famous name linked in every Scottish mind with the Forth railway bridge helped to build the road bridge— Sir William Arrol & Company. Together with the Cleveland Bridge & Engineering Company and Dorman Long, Arrol's formed a consortium called the A.C.D. Bridge Company, to tender for the bridge, and the tender was accepted. The contract for the substructure went to John Howard & Company Limited, and Reed & Mallik won that for the approach via-ducts to the main bridge. The northern approach roads were to be built by Whatlings Limited and those on the southern side by A. M. Carmichael & Company Limited.

Scottish folk could hardly believe their eyes as they watched the bridge-builders gather at the Queensferry and begin to spin the slender web across the estuary. The run to Queensferry had always been a favourite Sunday outing, but now the journey had a purpose—to see how "their" bridge was going.

The man in charge at Queensferry was H. Shirley-Smith, the A.C.D. Bridge Company's site agent, who had already worked on bridges in four continents—Europe, Africa, Asia and Aus-tralasia. He had been building bridges since 1923—in fact since the Forth Road Bridge was first mooted—and it almost seemed as if his career had been leading up to this silver link across the Firth. Shirley-Smith's book *The World's Great Bridges* describes his work, beginning at Sydney Harbour Bridge, and continuing by way of Southern Rhodesia, India, Siam, Nyasa-land, Finland and New Zealand.

Preliminary work at Queensferry began on 1 September 1958, and nearly three months later Mr. John Maclay went to Port Edgar to drive in the first pile and inaugurate the actual bridge construction. As the Secretary of State turned a valve a whoosh of compressed air and a clank of machinery set the five year task in motion, and Scotland sat back to watch pro-gress.

Handling the great engineering problems and the little army of men was not the most difficult part of bridging the Forth for a second time. The weather was by far the greatest problem the builders had to face, for at every season of the year storms whipped down the estuary to halt work for days on end.

"I have been all over the world," said Shirley-Smith in the latter part of 1963, "but I have never struck a site for weather like this. It's quite fantastic. There is no month in which we have lost less than 25 per cent of our time because of foul weather, quite apart from the third lost while cable spin-ning. And we're still losing a quarter of our time. God knows

what the weather will be like this winter. I only hope there's
fair weather for the opening a year from now."

The summers of 1961 and 1962 were among the windiest and
wettest experienced in many years, and the first months of
1963 brought the fiercest and longest drawn-out winter known
for nearly a century. In 1962, for example, winds of 100 to
120 miles an hour struck the bridge, breaking strands of the
cables which were being spun, blowing catwalks 60 or 70 feet
downstream, and destroying telephones, lights and winches.

The first part of the job was the £2,400,000 contract for the
substructure carried out by John Howard & Company, and
perhaps the most vital operation of all. The Mackintosh Rock
provided a firm enough footing for the northern pier and the
rock was levelled off some 25 feet below the surface, and a
huge 168-foot-long cofferdam floated out and sunk on the site
to build the foundation of the pier. On the south side the problem was much greater, for the riverbed was silt overlying gravel
and then boulder clay and rock. Here an artificial "rock" had
to be built and mortised into the bedrock. First two caissons to
exclude the water were towed into position and the water was
pumped out, so that silt and gravel could be removed to give
a firm basis in which the piers could be set.

The towers carrying the cables from which the bridge deck
would be suspended soared 512 feet into the air, high above
the cantilevers of the railway bridge, and each comprised eleven
sections, which were prefabricated at Arrol's Glasgow works,
down to the boltholes, fitted together and then taken apart for
transporting to the site.

As each of the segments was added a broad platform surrounding the tower was pushed upwards by means of hydraulic
jacks to provide a safe working platform for the men. And as
there was always greater risk attached to ascending and descend-
ing than to working aloft the men spent their entire working
day high in the tower, with a mess room on the platform in
which they could make tea, dry out their wet clothes, read,
chat, and eat hot meals sent up by a hoist from the site canteens.

As the towers neared their maximum height an odd and unexpected snag was encountered. Although the towers were

167

stable enough in gales an oscillation was set up when a gentle wind of 20 miles an hour was blowing in an east-west direction. The movement was several feet, building up over a few minutes and dying away, so that the erectors found it not only difficult to work but some were even seasick—500 feet above the river.

On Tuesday, 14 February 1961, the last segment of the northern tower was raised after a two-week wait until gales died down so that the operation could be carried out. This brought the height of the pillar to 505 feet, and left only the steel saddles for the cable to be added. The southern tower was well in hand, too, and this marked what should have been the half-way mark in the five-year schedule.

Shirley-Smith was satisfied with progress and wrote, "By the summer of 1963 impeded by nothing but tolls, traffic will start to flow across Britain's first major bridge of the motorway age."

Shirley-Smith had already encountered an impediment which was going to become increasingly irritating, and throw his schedule out by a whole year. The weather in the Forth estuary was still hampering the bridge-builders. On the next phase the 25 per cent loss of time increased to $33\frac{1}{3}$ per cent, and engineers admitted that they had never encountered such conditions anywhere in the world.

Great underground anchorages had been built for the main cables which were to be slung across the firth, and cable-spinning was now ready to start. Although it was called spinning, the wire was not twisted at all, but was made up of thousands of parallel wires compressed together and bound to form the thick cable. The process was invented by an American John A. Roebling in 1855, and it had been used in America for many years but this was the first time it had been adopted in Europe. The cables were to stretch 7,000 feet from anchorage to anchorage, and in all 11,618 parallel wires were to be spun into "ropes" two feet thick. It took 30,000 miles of galvanized wire, which was delivered in 10-hundredweight coils and spliced and rewound on to reels 7 feet in diameter.

Before cable-spinning began catwalks had to be built from which 150 men could help to guide the wires into position.

(*Left*) Strands of the cable emerge from the anchorage chamber which stretches deep into the earth. This is the entrance to the north-east anchorage chamber. (*Right*) 1962: some 400 feet above the River Forth men work on the catwalk as the spinning wheel carrying the strands of the cable passes overhead

By mid-1963 the majesty of the road bridge begins
still dominates the Inchgarvie narrows. Between

to show, but the railway bridge, now 73 years old,
the two the wash of the ferry is clearly visible

March, 1963, and the suspended structure is slowly extending further over the Forth. *(Below)* Autumn, 1963: the gap in the centre of the bridge is almost closed, and as the men work high above the Firth safety nets are slung underneath to protect them

The first wire for the catwalks and the first link between the two towers was erected on Wednesday, 11 July 1961. The river was officially closed to traffic and there was a moment of excitement as a pinnace from the Royal Navy station at Port Edgar sailed slowly downstream over the partly submerged cable, but neither vessel nor cable came to any harm. In the following weeks another twenty-one of these inch-thick cables were erected to support the two catwalks. The first strands of the main cable of the bridge were spun in November when four wires were secured to the underground anchorage on the south side and looped round the travelling wheel which was connected to a hauling rope. The rope was then set in motion, its speed synchronized with electrically-driven unreeling machines, and the wires were carried 512 feet high over the tips of the main towers to the far anchorage on the north shore. There the strands were anchored, and while the spinning wheel was returned empty, another with four more loops of wire was on its way from the south side. Within a month the cable was as thick as a lamp post and the spinning was going on for sixteen hours a day. Men stationed on the catwalks at intervals to ensure that the cable had the right degree of sag, were exposed to the winds which funnelled down the estuary. It was not a comfortable job—there were no tea breaks during the eight-hour shifts, and the only comfort for the men was hot soup which was distributed along the line.

"The men are working as happily as any can who are half frozen in a 50-mile-an-hour gale 500 feet above the Forth at midnight," said Shirley-Smith. And for this their wages, production bonus and height money totalled £35 a week.

One man who braved the climb 500 feet above the Forth was a sailor who missed the last ferry and calmly walked across the bridge-builders' catwalk.

By the time the last strand of the cables had been strung across the estuary in August 1962, the work had fallen well behind schedule and it was obvious that no motor-cars would cross the bridge in 1963.

From the cables steel wires to hold the carriageway were slung, and originally it had been intended to build the entire width of the deck at once, but wind tunnel tests showed that this might cause aerodynamic instability, so instead it was decided to erect the deck in two passes.

The steel for the deck was carried along jetties to the base of the towers and swung 150 feet up on to the deck, from where it was taken to the working face. Here the men had their headquarters and, just as in the towers, the little huts were home during the long, cold shift.

As the steelwork crept outwards from the main pillars it was noticed to turn upwards at the tip, and by the time it stretched a few hundred feet this upwards sweep was very marked and alarming to the uninitiated. The reasons were simply that the distribution of the weight was causing the towers to bend backwards slightly, thus raising the height of the main cables, and also to the fact that by the time the main cables were bearing the full weight of the deck of the bridge they would stretch 18 feet. So of course when the deck was only partly built they were not fully stretched. The first of the passes was completed in December 1963, and the second followed quickly. After that came the laying of the roadways, footpaths and cycle tracks.

One of the chief arguments of Lord Elgin for his Inchgarvie plan in 1944 had been the convenience of leading the approach to the bridge from the main Edinburgh–Queensferry road. Such a road would have proved quite inadequate for today's traffic, and in fact the original approaches had to be redesigned during the construction of the bridge. At South Queensferry it was decided to substitute flyovers for roundabouts, and on the northern side a cloverleaf junction was built. Because of the hilly ground eight specially designed approaches had to be built leading to the northern cloverleaf, and because of this it became nicknamed the Octopus. Another ominous decision for those who were opposed to tolls, was that made in the autumn of 1961 to incorporate an "electric blanket" under the road surface to provide a safe braking area at the approaches to the toll zone.

Of course in a construction job like the road bridge there are risks, but these were cut to a minimum. Safety was drilled into the men and their leaders at all times and precautions were rigidly enforced. No one, whether worker or visitor, was allowed on to the bridge without a bright blue A.C.D. Company safety helmet, for a small piece of metal or a bolt dropped from the towers could kill or severely injure a man. Safety harness had to be worn at all times when working in an exposed position, too, but the piece of safety equipment which caught the public imagination was the great safety nets which were slung below the decking as men were working far out over the firth. The bridge-building company spent £20,000 on these nets which followed the progress of the bridge decking and they proved their worth a number of times. More remarkable still was the fact that a workman fell from the bridge, missed the nets and lived.

It is undoubtedly due to the care taken that no more than one man was killed while construction was in progress compared with the fifty-seven who died on the railway bridge.

At last a comparison between the twin bridges of the Forth has crept in—the only surprising aspect being that it did not do so earlier, for the temptation to compare the two is great. The new bridge for example, contains only 39,000 tons of steel compared with the 50,000 tons in the old one, and 250 to 300 men have built it against the 4,000 to 5,000 on the railway one.

The greatest difference of all, however, lies in the way in which the two bridges came about. The railway one was the product of a few men working, if not actually against the wishes of a great many people then without their support. Today's road bridge on the other hand is a triumph of the people of Scotland over a reluctant Government. It is a splendid victory after a battle fought for close on half a century.

CHAPTER FIFTEEN

TOLLS OR NO TOLLS?

WHEN Inglis Kerr called his Press conference at the Hawes Inn in 1923 the cost of the bridge was estimated to be £2,500,000 to £3,000,000. A decade later the figure was around £4,000,000; in the early post-war years it was £6,000,000; by the time work was begun it had more than doubled, and now the bill, when it is all totted up is expected to be more than £20,000,000. How can such a sum be paid?

The answer, which kept recurring, was by tolls, and tolls became almost as great an issue as the building of the bridge had been. Even though they were told that other parts of the country would soon have toll bridges, the large majority of Scotsmen answered that they were being singled out for unfair treatment.

Tolls were suggested almost from the start, and there was a good Scot who could be quoted in their favour. Adam Smith had said: "When the carriages which pass over a highway or a bridge, and the lighters which sail upon a navigable canal, pay toll in proportion to their weight or their tonnage, they pay for the maintenance of those public works exactly in proportion to the wear and tear which they occasion of them. . . . It seems scarce possible to invent a more equitable method of raising a tax."

However, it was not necessary to go back to Adam Smith for a precedent; tolls had been used successfully in the United States and there a great many bridges had been built in the twentieth century, whereas none of similar magnitude had gone up in Britain.

The Joint Committee of Inquiry also had suggested tolls as a possible means of financing the project. In fact, opinion was generally that a toll bridge would be better than no bridge at all. Thus it was accepted early on that the road bridge might be a toll bridge.

When Arthur Woodburn raised the question of the bridge in the Commons in February 1945, he suggested that if Scotland had to build the bridge herself, £300,000 a year could be brought in by a three shilling toll.

"You are not suggesting a toll bridge?" asked a fellow Member in astonishment.

"If it is necessary, yes," replied Woodburn.

It is not surprising, therefore, that when the Government at last agreed to authorize the starting of the work that it offered to lend the bulk of the money on the understanding that it would be repaid from tolls.

William Hamilton, Member of Parliament for West Fife, told the House that there was great disatisfaction throughout Scotland over the tolls proposal—a statement which brought "Ohs" from the Government side and a protest from Sir William Anstruther Gray that there would be a large measure of support for the Government in the stand it was taking on tolls.

This "large measure of support" was not apparent in Scotland, where opinion hardened against tolls as the bridge took shape. True Scotland had agreed to tolls, but a number of people felt that conditions had changed since then, particularly in Fife where huge redundancies took place in the county's basic industry—coalmining. The county was classified as a Development Area and in view of this it seemed incongruous to the authorities in the Kingdom that tolls should be exacted from the county's industries. Furthermore, it seemed hard that tolls should be insisted on for an area experiencing economic crisis while other gigantic schemes, such as the motorways and the Whiteinch Tunnel at Glasgow, were free.

Nigel Tranter's National Committee took up the subject with Maclay in the spring of 1961 only to be told that the Government's policy was that where the additional convenience to road users was very great in comparison with existing facilities it was appropriate that the road users should pay. Tranter pointed out the incongruity of this in view of such improvements at the Doncaster by-pass and the M1, and asked: "Why should a road be singled out just because it crosses water? Scotland, with immeasurably more rivers and sea lochs to cross, is bound to be grievously penalized under this new and curious policy."

Again Tranter took up his pen when Edinburgh Town Council reversed its earlier decision on tolls and agreed to support the other local authorities in urging abandonment of them. Writing to *The Scotsman* he described tolls as "a stagecoach anachronism in the road system".

In support of this letter Fife County Convener, Mr. John McWilliam, wrote that although the decision to impose tolls was still legally binding Edinburgh's decision brought unanimity among the authorities involved.

"To impose tolls on the one major artery created north of the Forth since the Kincardine Bridge (in 1936!) would, in our opinion be one more rivet—and a vital one—in the wall which divides the reasonably prosperous from the unreasonably poor. . . . Is it too much to hope that Mr. Noble (The Secretary of State) and his talented servants will do the 'big' thing and squash tolls for ever?"

Shirley-Smith, Agent of the A.C.D. Bridge Company came to the support of tolls. He wrote: "When the Forth and Severn Bridges are completed they will together collect toll revenue of the order of £2,000,000 per annum which will go straight to the Exchequer. The cost of building the Forth Road Bridge has been about £2,000,000 per annum, and the cost of the Severn Bridge, which is following on will be much the same. When the Government come to build the next big bridge they will not, therefore, have to find the money out of revenue from taxation, because they will be getting repayment of debt from the tolls. This may somewhat over simplify what is a very complex matter, but it would seem to be a fair interpretation of the position.

"There is no doubt that everyone would prefer free bridges to toll bridges, but bitter experience shows that in practice the choice lies between a toll bridge or no bridge at all. No big bridge was built in Great Britain for seventy years after the Forth Railway Bridge was completed, because the principle of toll bridges was not accepted. During this period in the United States some forty great bridges were built, all as financially self-liquidating projects to be paid for by means of tolls. These have paid their way handsomely from the start, none has got into financial difficulties, and on some the toll charges have been successively reduced.

"In practice it is found that these great toll projects not only carry the existing traffic from car ferries, etc., that is diverted over them, but also generate traffic, to the extent of from 50 per cent to 250 per cent more, which they attract by reason of the convenience of the new crossing."

If big bridges are costly utilities, the Fife County Convener asked in reply, what then are the M1, and other motorways, the £10,000,000 River Clyde tunnel at Whiteinch, the Hammersmith Flyover, the Hyde Park Underpass, and many other road schemes. "How is it possible to finance these without tolls and yet say it is impossible in the case of the road bridge?"

"It is worth repeating," he continued, "that once a project has been financed in Britain, the cost has already been met by the general body of taxpayers. It is fully accepted as a standard principle of public finance that the provision of money by the state in this country is in a totally different category from the provision of money by industrial firms, building societies, public bodies, individuals or local authorities for that matter.

"Put shortly, the latter can be said to be controlled by money, whereas the state is the one body in the country that is in control of money, and has, in addition, the entire and unified taxable capacity of the country at its command. For this reason it is irrelevant and misleading to apply ordinary commercial principles to the Forth Road Bridge project any more than they can be applied to schools or hospitals.

"The provision of the bridge is a public service in the same way as all other public services, including other forms of road building. There is absolutely no reason why this particular project should be singled out for extra taxation."

The Burgh Treasurer of Dunfermline joined in, also, and pointed out that because the taxpayers of Britain are one body, paying taxes under one system, as opposed to the American federal system, we are able to look at the tolls in an entirely different light from the United States.

Shirley-Smith retorted point by point to Mr. McWilliam:

"1. None of the bridges he mentions as special utilities cost anything like as much as the Forth Road Bridge.

"2. He fails to mention the Mersey Tunnel (1934) a toll project on which the traffic increased fourfold in twenty years, and which is now filled to capacity.

"3. My argument is not confined to the U.S.A. No long span bridge has been built in any country in the world in the last twenty years that was not a toll bridge. The recent Auckland Harbour Bridge in New Zealand and Tancarville Bridge in France are most successful toll bridges, with traffic far exceeding the estimates. The proposed huge new bridges at Lisbon, the Messina Straits, and the Bosphorus are also to be toll projects.

"4. No big toll bridge in the world had ever been boycotted by traffic, and it is quite absurd to suggest such a happening over the Forth.

"5. Mr. McWilliam or his forebears and others who supported toll-free bridges had seventy years since the railway bridge was built in which to get the Forth Road Bridge started. But they failed. Within a year or two after it was proposed to finance the bridge by tolls the building began. Is this not a complete answer to the case?"

It may have been the bridge-builder's answer, but it did not satisfy the Scottish public, who were cynical about the prospect of tolls once imposed ever being abolished when they had achieved their purpose. On our comparable utility, the Mersey Tunnel, tolls are still levied although the tunnel must have been paid for two or three times over, and that perhaps is the real reason for the Scottish public's fear of a toll system to pay for the bridge. They fear that they will be paying years after every penny of the construction bill has been paid back.

In 1963 the Road Bridge Joint Committee had to face up

to tolls as a point on which the Government would not give way, and at a meeting towards the end of August a sub-committee recommended a flat rate toll of half-a-crown despite protests from Lord Provost Duncan M. Weatherstone of Edinburgh that this was unrealistic. Although this meeting was held in private the decision leaked to the Press, and the Lord Provost began the October meeting with a rebuke for Mr. Peter Walker, Convener of West Lothian County Council and Mr. John McWilliam, Convener of Fife.

After the storm of the August Press leak, the Lord Provost moved an amendment that the Board should back a flat rate charge of four shillings, or alternatively 3s. 6d. for motor-cars with proportionate increases for other vehicles. A half-crown toll was based on "wishful thinking", he said, and in pushing for such a low charge the Fife Convener was "fighting a rearguard action". Edinburgh's Town Clerk and City Chamberlain had examined the problem and consultants had been brought in, and the Lord Provost had based his figures on their findings.

The lower toll had been based on a £12,500,000 loan to be repaid over thirty years at $6\frac{1}{4}$ per cent, and was calculated on an 8 per cent growth of traffic with an initial volume of five million vehicles, rising to eleven million. The amount needed from the Government could rise to £15,000,000, and even the tolls committee did not dispute this.

"I am not an unqualified supporter of the Secretary of State in this or any other Government, but this is the position as I understand it," he said.

In reply Mr. McWilliam told the board that while he respected the views of the technical advisers on this matter, they could be nothing more than opinions, which generally tended to be cautious and conservative.

"A half-crown is just as likely to be an over-estimate as an under-estimate. We are not talking of a personal or a private investment. It is a public investment—and investment for Scotland."

If the loan should exceed £12,500,000, as it seemed certain to do, then he suggested that the Board should go to the

Secretary of State and ask for more time to pay the money back.

The Board backed this move to keep the tolls within reasonable proportions, and by ten votes to three it decided to recommend to the Secretary of State a flat rate toll of half-a-crown.

As the Board wrangled the bridge-builders pushed on with the two great spans which reached out like arms, raised slightly in salute, to meet towards the end of the year. The bridge was at least within sight of completion, and it could only be a matter of time—and a short time at that—before it would be ready to receive the first vehicles hurrying between Fife and Lothian.

Underneath the bridge the ferries continued to ply, their days numbered. The Forth Road Bridge Order Confirmation Act of 1947 made a statutory provision for the ferry to be abandoned when the road bridge opened, thus ending the 800-year-old story of the ferry. Since long before the days when saintly Margaret hied over the estuary to give the ferry its name, these narrows at Inchgarvie have witnessed much of the history of Scotland pass by, and the fragments left to us reveal how it touched the lives of kings and common people alike.

Progress brings to an end the Queensferry story and, although Scots have fought so hard and so long for this bridge, their joy at taking the new highway to Fife is tinged with sadness, as they see the empty piers and the estuary without the little ships bobbing from one Queensferry to the other, gleaming in summer sunlight, or shrinking under the lee of the railway bridge in wintry weather.

Even those who sat so impatiently in their motor-cars may sigh for a sight of the Queen's Ferry.

178

Bibliography

This book has been written principally from newspaper cuttings, official reports, petitions, and contemporary books. I am especially indebted to the following:

Alloa Journal
The Bulletin
Dundee Advertiser
Dunfermline Journal
Dunfermline Press
Edinburgh Evening News
The Engineer
Engineering
The Glasgow Herald
Herepath's Railway Journal

The Illustrated London News
The Observer
The Railway Magazine
The Railway News
The Railway Record
The Railway Times
The Scots Magazine
The Scotsman
Stirling Sentinel
The Times

Anderson, J., *Report on Bridge of Chains to be Thrown over the Firth of Forth at Queensferry,* 1818.

Balingall, William, *Shores of Fife,* 1872.

Barlow, C., *The New Tay Bridge,* 1889.

Bruce, J., *Tullis's Guide to the Edinburgh and Northern Railway,* 1848.

Bryce, D. & Son (Publishers), *Graphic Guide to Edinburgh, the Forth Bridge and the International Exhibition,* 1890.
Burntisland Official Guide.

Cadell, H. M., *The Story of the Forth,* 1913.

Cunningham, A. S., *Inverkeithing, North Queensferry and Limekilns,* 1897.

Dick, S., *Pageant of the Forth,* 1910.

Duckworth, C. L. D. and Langmuir, G. E., *Railway and Other Steamers,* 1948.

179

FERRIES

Buchanan, G., "Report on the Erecting of Low Water Landing Places on the Coast between Kinghorn and Pettycur," 1827.

Greenhill, A., "Minutes of his Treaty with the Committee of Ferry Trustees," 1826.

Mackgill, D. M., "Statement in Reference to the Improvement of the Fife–Midlothian Ferry," 1838.

"Report by Committee Appointed by the Managing Trustees of the Queensferry Passage," 1828.

"Memorandum for the Consideration of the Fife Ferry Trustees," 1826.

"Report Respecting the Lower Ferry between the Counties of Midlothian and Fife," 1828.

Smith, G., "Burntisland Ferry," 1837.

Telford, T., "Report on lower ferry," 1826.

FORTH ROAD BRIDGE

"Forth Road Bridge (Local Authorities) Joint Committee, Economic Justification of the Forth Road Bridge," 1936.

"Forth Road Bridge (Local Authorities) Joint Committee, Modern History of the Forth Road Bridge Project and Historical Statement as to the Ferry at Queensferry," 1936.

Scottish Home Department. "Reports on the Proposed Underwater Crossing of the Forth and the Forth Bridge Scheme," 1956.

Grieve, J., Taylor J., and Vazie, W., "Report on Practicability of making a tunnel under the River Forth," 1806.

Granton Harbour Handbook, 1956.

"Joint Report of Mott, Hay & Anderson and Sir Alexander Gibb & Partners regarding the Proposals for the Construction of a Road Bridge across the River Forth at Alloa or Kincardine," 1930.

Kincardine-on-Forth Road Bridge. Souvenir of Opening, 1936.

Lewin, H. G., *Early British Railways*, 1925.

Lewin, H. G., *The Railway Mania and its Aftermath*, 1936.

Mackay, A. J. G., *A Sketch of the History of Fife and Kinross*, 1890.

Mackay, T., *Life of Fowler,* 1900.

Millar, J. and Vazie, W., "Observations on the Practicability of making Tunnels under navigable rivers particularly applicable to the proposed tunnel under the Forth," 1807.

Phillips, P., *The Forth Bridge.*

Purvis, Sir R., Arrol, Sir William, *A Memoir,* 1913.

"Report on Surveys for the Tunnel under the River Forth," 1806.

"Report on the Tay Bridge Disaster," 1880.

Stephen, W., *History of Inverkeithing and Rosyth,* 1921.

Westhofen, W., *The Forth Bridge,* 1890.

Index